CHOICE MENUS

An Easy Guide with Recipes
for Healthy Everyday Meal Planning

Marjorie Hollands, M.Sc., R.P.Dt., C.D.E.

Margaret Howard, B.Sc., R.P.Dt., P.H.Ec.

MACMILLAN CANADA
A Division of Canada Publishing Corporation
Toronto, Ontario, Canada

Canadian Cataloguing in Publication Data

Hollands, Marjorie, 1930 –

Choice menus

Includes index.
ISBN 0-7715-9167-5

1. Diabetes – Diet therapy – Recipes. I. Howard, Margaret, 1930– . II. Canadian Diabetes Association. III. Title

RC662.H64 1993   641.5'6314   C92–095417–0

Macmillan Canada wishes to thank the Canada Council and the Ontario Ministry of Culture and Communications for supporting its publishing program.

Macmillan Canada
A Division of Canada Publishing Corporation
Toronto, Canada

1   2   3   4   5   BP   97   96   95   94   93

Printed in Canada

PAGE DESIGN AND COMPOSITION: Joseph Gisini, Andrew Smith Graphics Inc.

FRONT COVER: Baked chicken with crispy coating (page 91).
BACK COVER: Cheesecake with fresh fruit (page 98).

CONTENTS

AUTHORS' ACKNOWLEDGEMENTS

We would like to thank the following people who have given guidance, encouragement and hours of their time towards the creation of this book.

Jan Eno, for the initial encouragement to write *Choice Menus*.

The staff at the National Office of the Canadian Diabetes Association, in particular, Melanie Wanless and Sue Boyd, for their cooperation in helping make this book possible.

Members of the National Nutrition Committee (NNC) of the Canadian Diabetes Association, and colleagues who applied their expertise to the review of our manuscript: Phyllis Duxbury, present NNC chair, Peggy Dunbar, Ann Fox, Alexandra Jenkins, Pat Redman, our NNC liaison, and Janie Sanderson.

The staff of Macmillan of Canada: Denise Schon and Kirsten Hanson, for counsel and editorial support; Janice Brett, for coordinating the production of this challenging book.

Andrew Smith Graphics Inc., for the design and consultation on food photographs.

Barbara Selley and Sharyn Joliat at Info Access (1988) Inc. for their advice and expert nutritional analysis of the recipes and menus.

Kathy Younker-Smith, for verifying recipe Food Choice values with humour and words of wisdom, and for review of the manuscript.

The many TRIDEC (Tri-Hospital Diabetes Education Centre, Women's College Hospital) graduates over the years who shared their feelings about food and about diabetes and were the inspiration for Choice Menus.

Our many friends for their interest and support and recipe ideas.

Special thanks to our two families, the Howards and the Hollands, who listened, tasted the recipes and continued to show interest throughout the book's development. A very special thanks to Margaret's husband John for his hours of editorial assistance.

To everyone who uses *Choice Menus*, we hope that it will help simplify healthy meal planning and at the same time add to your enjoyment of good food.

We gratefully acknowledge the three corporate sponsors whose financial support made menu and recipe analysis and the unique, but expensive, format of this book possible: Miles Canada Inc. (Pharmaceutical Division), the Canadian Sugar Institute, and Kraft General Foods. We also appreciate the generous access by Kraft General Foods, Fred Bird and Wm.R.Trought Management Inc. to their food photography libraries.

And a final thank you to the happy coincidence that placed the two of us in the same class at the University of Western Ontario and later at Toronto General Hospital, leading to our lifelong friendship and this book.

PREFACE

Choice Menus is a unique guide to healthy eating. It is not just another cookbook, nor will it cause you pangs of guilt because you find many of your favourite meals and foods on the restricted list. Instead, it provides you with a month of menus with supporting recipes, in a plan in which balance and moderation are the basis for healthy eating. *Choice Menus* can be a guide for anyone interested in everyday meal planning.

The book is motivated, however, by the authors' desire to help the person, or others preparing meals for the person with or likely to develop non-insulin dependent diabetes mellitus (Type 2 Diabetes).

For many, the risk of developing insulin insufficiency and the consequent lack of control of blood glucose arises from a lifestyle and eating pattern that leads to an excess of body fat and subjects the body to a fasting and gorging regimen that taxes its metabolic machinery to the limit. *Choice Menus* will help you break this eating pattern and put into action a strategy of prevention, or management, of non-insulin dependent diabetes. For those with Type 2 diabetes, this guide supports, but does not replace, individualized meal plans and counselling, and recognizes that diet is the cornerstone of management.

Choice Menus is based on current expert advice on healthy eating. It translates a number of nutritional recommendations, including Canada's Guidelines for Healthy Eating (1990), Canada's Food Guide (1992), and Guidelines for the Management of Diabetes Mellitus in the 1990s (1989), into actual real-life meals and menus for every day, and indeed for several months. By following the varied menu plan, you can take the guesswork out of counting calories, using the CDA Food Choice System, and obtaining a balanced diet providing all the essential nutrients but reduced in fat and energy. And the authors recognize that (nearly) all our familiar foods can fit into a menu plan that will help prevent or manage Type 2 diabetes. For example, desserts, low in fat, are not forgotten in meal planning. Added sugars, up to 10% of the total dietary calories, are permitted, recognizing the current recommendations of the Canadian Diabetes Association on the Role of Dietary Sugars in Diabetes Mellitus (1992). What is emphasized, however, is a distribution of the daily calories among all three meals of the day. In addition, *Choice Menus* emphasizes slowly digested starchy foods and high fibre daily menus, but you won't even notice because your familiar foods are there!

I'm confident that *Choice Menus* will assist you to take control and have a healthy eating pattern.

G. Harvey Anderson, Ph.D.
PROFESSOR, NUTRITIONAL SCIENCES AND PHYSIOLOGY,
ACTING DEAN, FACULTY OF MEDICINE,
UNIVERSITY OF TORONTO

NUTRIENT ANALYSIS OF RECIPES AND MENUS

Nutrient analysis of recipes and menus was carried out by Info Access (1988) Inc. using the Nutritional Accounting component of CBORD Menu Management System and the Canadian Nutrient File (1988) supplemented with data from the 1991 release. Fibre values were obtained from the 1988 version of the Canadian Nutrient File. Analysis was based on Imperial measures and on the number of servings specified. The analyses take into account cooking methods, yields and associated changes in nutrient composition. Recipe variations were averaged only when ingredient food values were similar.

Unless otherwise stated, recipes were tested and analyzed using 2% milk, 2% yogurt and 2% cottage cheese. Fat and calories can be further reduced by substituting either 1% or skim milk products. All menus can be assumed to include 2 tbsp (25 mL) milk for tea or coffee whenever milk is not included as a beverage. All canned fruit specified in menus and recipes refers to fruit canned in fruit juice.

Microwave recipes were tested in a 700-watt, full-size microwave oven. If oven is different, cooking times may have to be adjusted slightly.

Food Choice values were assigned according to Canadian Diabetes Association guidelines, with carbohydrate calculated as total carbohydrate minus dietary fibre. Total carbohydrate and dietary fibre are stated separately in nutrient information given with each recipe.

Menus were analyzed using serving sizes specified in the Good Health Eating Guide published by the Canadian Diabetes Association (1982).

CANADIAN DIABETES ASSOCIATION

For further information about diabetes, write to the Canadian Diabetes Association Divisional Office nearest you. There are 10 divisional offices, with 170 branches across Canada.

BRITISH COLUMBIA/YUKON
1091 West 8th Avenue
Vancouver, British Columbia
V6H 2V3
(604) 732-1331

ALBERTA/N.W.T.
#305, 10240-124th Street
Edmonton, Alberta
T5N 3W6 (403) 482-2307

SASKATCHEWAN
2301 Avenue C. N., Suite 104
Saskatoon, Saskatchewan
S7L 5Z5
(306) 933-1238

MANITOBA
283 Portage Avenue
Winnipeg, Manitoba
R3B 2B5
(204) 943-7529

ONTARIO
15 Toronto Street
Toronto, Ontario
M5C 2R1
(416) 362-4440

QUEBEC
180 boulevard René-Lévesque est
bureau 200
Montréal, Quebec
H2X 1N6
(514) 398-0954

NEW BRUNSWICK/NOUVEAU BRUNSWICK
259 Brunswick, Suite 105
Fredericton, N.B.
E3B 1G8
(506) 452-9009

NOVA SCOTIA
1221 Barrington Street
Halifax, Nova Scotia
B3J 1Y2
(902) 421-1444

PRINCE EDWARD ISLAND
Box 133
Charlottetown, P. E. I.
C1A 7K2
(902) 894-3005

NEWFOUNDLAND/LABRADOR
Box 9130
St. John's, Newfoundland
A1A 2X3
(709) 754-0953

Canadian Diabetes Association National Office
15 Toronto Street, Toronto, Ontario
M5C 2R1
(416) 362-4440

INTRODUCTION

Maybe you have learned you have diabetes or your blood sugar is a bit too high. Maybe you have been told to lose some weight because there is a good chance you will develop Type 2 diabetes if you don't. Maybe it's a family member or a friend who has diabetes, and you don't know what foods to serve them. Maybe you want to be healthier and need to change your eating habits to achieve it. Whatever the case, *Choice Menus* comes to your rescue.

Choice Menus is not just another cookbook. It offers 104 healthy and tasty menus that you can "mix and match" to take the guesswork out of managing diabetes and planning meals. It contains more than 100 delicious and easy-to-prepare recipes, with variations, to use with the menus. We believe *Choice Menus* will find a place in your kitchen, not just on your book shelf. It will be your ready source of inspiration when you ask yourself, "What am I going to eat today?"

Making food choices and planning menus can sometimes be frustrating and tedious. *Choice Menus* will make this much easier. It is written for all those searching for a healthy eating style who have said to their dietitian/nutritionist, "Couldn't you just write me out a month of menus?"

Many of the menus are simple and quickly prepared. Others are more elaborate and may be the ones you choose when you have more time or are entertaining. Many need no special recipes. Other menus are supported by wonderful new recipes we know will become family favourites.

The Special Occasions menus and recipes will convince friends and relatives, once and for all, that healthy eating can include tasty and attractive meals everyone enjoys.

All the menus are based on the Canadian Diabetes Association's Food Choice System and are planned especially for someone with Type 2 diabetes. Recipes also include Food Choice Values so they can be used in menus you plan yourself.

Choice Menus is not intended to replace the meal plan prepared by a dietitian/nutritionist. It is meant to be used with a meal plan to give variety and fresh ideas. Meal planning and Food Choices are often confusing at first. The goal of *Choice Menus* is to make meal planning simpler.

If you have Type 1 (insulin-dependent) diabetes, your insulin action may require a different meal pattern than is used in our menus. Consult your dietitian about how to make adjustments.

Choice Menus allows you to choose the calorie level that best meets your energy needs. Any day's combination of breakfast, lunch and dinner menus provides 1200 calories. Adding one or more snacks will increase your daily intake to 1500 or 1800 calories a day. If weight loss is your goal, most forty-plus women need about 1800 calories to maintain their present weight, so 1200 or 1500 calories will result in gradual weight loss. Men usually need around 2000 to 2200 calories of food energy and will lose weight on 1500 to 1800 calories per day. Check with your doctor or dietitian if you are not sure which calorie level is best for you. No matter which meals you choose during the day, they will be balanced to provide 50% of the calories from carbohydrate, 20% from protein and 30% from fat. This is ideal for the person with Type 2 diabetes, for the person who needs to lose weight and for the person who wishes to adopt a healthier way of eating.

Tips for Healthy Eating

Healthy eating is not nearly as difficult as it sometimes seems. Healthy eating is about making better food choices most of the time, not necessarily all of the time. To illustrate, some of our Special Occasion, Snack and dining-out menus contain more fat and sodium than we would normally recommend. This reflects the real world in which we all eat. However, in each of these instances, total calories and carbohydrate remain the same as in the other menus.

The menus and recipes contained in *Choice Menus*, as well as supporting diabetes recommendations, reflect Canada's Guidelines for Healthy Eating, published by Health and Welfare Canada in March 1990. These are:

1. Enjoy a variety of food.

Eating different foods prepared in various ways every day ensures you get all the vitamins and minerals you need. Our menus include extensive variety while keeping price and availability in mind.

2. Emphasize cereals, breads, other grain products, vegetables and fruits.

These easy-on-the-budget foods are satisfying and low in fat. They belong to the complex carbohydrate family of foods. The beauty of complex carbohydrates is their tendency to be high in fibre. When you choose one, you get the other—an advantage both for healthy eating and particularly for diabetes control. But how much you eat matters since these foods do affect your blood sugar. *(See page 12.)*

3. Choose lower-fat dairy products, leaner meats and foods prepared with little or no fat.

Fat is fattening. There are 9 calories in 1 gram of fat compared with 4 calories in 1 gram of protein or carbohydrate.

To minimize fat:

• Use as little butter, margarine, oil and salad dressing as possible in cooking and at the table.

• Trim and discard visible fat from meats and use a nonstick skillet. If you don't have a nonstick skillet, now is the time to buy one.

• Select lower-fat cheeses. Look on labels for those with a milk fat or butterfat (MF or BF) content of 20% or less. "Light" Cheddar does not refer to the colour of the cheese but to its lower fat content.

• Use lower-fat milk and yogurt. Our menus and recipes use milk and yogurt; 1% and skim provide an even greater reduction in fat. The following table illustrates how calories increase with butter fat (BF) content.

½ cup (125 mL) skim milk or yogurt = 40 calories
½ cup (125 mL) 1% BF milk or yogurt = 50 calories
½ cup (125 mL) 2% BF milk or yogurt = 60 calories
½ (125 mL) cup homo milk = 80 calories

Our recipes in *Choice Menus* give many other taste-tempting ways to add flavour and moisture to foods while reducing fat.

4. Achieve and maintain a healthy body weight by enjoying regular physical activity and healthy eating.

Achieving a healthy body weight is important for all of us, but it is particularly important if you are overweight and have diabetes. Often a loss of as little as 10 pounds can improve blood glucose and cholesterol values. Wise eating habits, as promoted in *Choice Menus*, along with daily exercise such as walking, can help you reach and maintain a healthy weight.

5. Limit salt, alcohol and caffeine.

Keep the salt shaker off the table, particularly if you have high blood pressure. Add a very small amount during cooking if you must have salt, or substitute herbs and spices as we have in many of our recipes. Canned soups and bouillon mixes are often quite salty. Look for low-salt varieties or make your own broth. *(See page 63.)*

If you drink alcohol, limit yourself to one, or at the most two drinks on an occasion. More information appears in our Special Occasions section *(page 108)*. If you are a coffee drinker, current recommendations are to limit yourself to four cups a day.

Carbohydrate

Sugars and starches belong to the carbohydrate family. All carbohydrate is digested or broken down inside the body and is absorbed as simple sugars, ending up in the bloodstream as blood glucose. The faster a carbohydrate food digests, the faster the glucose is released and the faster the rise in blood glucose. People with diabetes may experience an increase in blood glucose after a meal that is greater than their bodies' own insulin supply can handle effectively.

If you have diabetes, the following suggestions are useful in helping control the effect of carbohydrate on blood glucose.

• Three or more moderate-sized meals a day are better handled by a limited insulin supply than one or two larger ones.

• Eating foods that are slowly digested can slow the rate of increase in blood glucose after a meal. Fruits and vegetables digest more slowly than juice. Foods containing soluble fibre digest more slowly than those that don't.

• Sugar eaten as part of a slowly digested meal enters the bloodstream more slowly than sugar taken as part of a beverage on an empty stomach.

Since people with Type 2 diabetes do not tolerate glucose very well, they need to limit the amount of glucose-producing foods (carbohydrate) eaten at *each meal*. Our menus are planned with these limits in mind, so *how much* is eaten is important.

Fibre

Many starchy foods, fruits and vegetables contain soluble or insoluble fibre.

After it is eaten, soluble fibre forms a sticky gel. This slows the digestion of starch, thereby slowing the rise in blood glucose after a meal. It is also thought to lower high cholesterol levels.
Key sources of soluble fibre are:
• oat bran and barley
• legumes such as lentils, dried beans and dried peas
• grain-based foods such as breads, cereals and pastas
• pectin-rich fruits such as apples, peaches, pears, strawberries and citrus fruits

Foods that contain insoluble fibre are full of "roughage" and so are great laxative foods. Roughage is thought to be important in preventing certain cancers.

Key sources of insoluble fibre are:
• wheat bran and foods made with wheat bran
• unpeeled fruits and vegetables
• foods containing whole grains and seeds

Sugars and Diabetes

Sugar appears in many different forms in the foods we eat: glucose and fructose in honey and corn syrup; glucose, fructose and sucrose in all fruits and vegetables; lactose in milk; maltose in beer. The sugar in the sugar bowl is pure sucrose, a sugar that occurs naturally in all living plants. It is most abundant in sugar cane and sugar beets. When the juice from these two plants is crystallized, the result is table sugar.

For generations, table sugar has been the sweetener of choice. Unfortunately, sugar has also been seen as a forbidden food and a guilty pleasure for those with a sweet tooth and diabetes. Persons with diabetes have traditionally been told to avoid sugar, because of the popular belief that it worsens diabetes control. This is just one of the myths about sugar and diabetes. Two others are:

MYTH: Eating too much sugar causes diabetes.
FACT: There is no scientific evidence that links sugar intake to the development of diabetes. However, whether they eat sugar or not, overweight people have an increased chance of developing Type 2 diabetes, especially if there is diabetes in the family.

MYTH: Sweet foods are fattening because sugar is high in calories.
FACT: Any food eaten in excess of energy needs can cause weight gain. Sugar itself is not fattening. The villain in high-calorie foods is usually fat, not sugar. Sugar has less than half the calories of fat; 4 calories per gram versus 9 calories per gram for fat. People who need to lose weight to bring their diabetes under control would be wiser to limit fat rather than act as if only sugar mattered.

The position of the Canadian Diabetes Association is that sugar need not be eliminated from the diabetic diet. It can be included as long as amounts are monitored, as for any other food item. The key is to eat foods containing small amounts of sugar as part of a slowly digested meal.

The use of added sugar in *Choice Menus* follows the guidelines of the Canadian Diabetes Association. That is, up to 10% of total energy (calories) eaten in a day may be sucrose or other added sugars. A person eating 1500 calories a day (three meals and one snack) is thus allowed 150 calories as sugar (10%). This is equal to about 35 to 40 grams of sugar *over the day*. Considering that the sugar intake of the Canadian population as a whole is about 12% of total calories, you can see that a diabetes diet is not that different.

Our menus limit sucrose to 10 grams in any one meal or snack, and follow the principle that *when* sugar is consumed matters as much as *how much*. Carbohydrate, including sugar, is spread evenly over the day, as part of slowly digested meals.

The recipes in *Choice Menus* use sugar as the sweetener whenever possible because it adds a flavour and texture to food that is hard to replace with a sugar substitute. We have also used honey to achieve a particular flavour result. Both are counted in the carbohydrate content allowed for a meal. In some instances, artificial sweeteners have been added to give more sweetness without adding more calories.

Artificial Sweeteners

Artificial sweeteners such as cyclamate, saccharin and aspartame have no effect on blood sugar and contain very few, if any, calories. Very small amounts are needed to provide flavour since they are usually many times sweeter than sucrose. Persons with diabetes can safely use this group of sweeteners. However, many people find their taste too different from the traditional sugar flavour they are used to. Artificial sweeteners may also lack the "bulk" or volume that sugar provides, resulting in poor texture and consistency in baked goods.

Choice Menus recipes were developed and tested using cyclamate or heat-stable aspartame.

Other Sweeteners

Fructose and sorbitol are examples of another group of sweeteners that do provide calories. They are often used in dietetic candies, chocolate and cookies when the texture and taste of sugar is desired. They are all right to use in small amounts but must be counted as part of the carbohydrate content of a meal. Corn syrup containing fructose and glucose is sometimes used as a replacement for sugar in soft drinks. These products all provide calories and may affect blood sugar levels as much as sucrose when used in excess. They therefore offer no special advantage in a diabetes diet.

Discuss the use of any added sugar with your dietitian, especially if you have very high triglycerides or if your diabetes is badly out of control.

HOW TO USE THIS BOOK

You will find over a month of "choice menus" in the next section: our choice and now yours. But first, find a home on your kitchen counter for your "easy guide with recipes for healthy everyday meal planning." This is not a book to be kept on a shelf for only an occasional glance. You will want to have it where you can refer to it every day.

In the following split page section, there are 32 tempting breakfast menus, 32 ideas for lunch, 32 complete dinner menus and a variety of snacks to fill the gap between meals. Most of the first menus you come to need no special recipes, or only simple ones described in the menu itself. Further along, menus call for the more detailed recipes you will find in the recipe section of the book.

The book's mix-and-match format provides maximum flexiblility. You may decide to follow each day's menu in sequence, or you may flip back and forth between menus for added variety. There may be days when you decide to use a dinner menu at noon and a lunch menu at suppertime. It's your choice! Any breakfast, lunch, dinner or combination of snacks will add up to the same number of calories. (See page 99 for more about snacking.) You will, no doubt, repeat favourite menus over and over, or you may have the same lunch several days in a row to use up a dish! Just keep in mind that variety is the spice of life and the key to healthy eating. *(See page 9)*

Many people are confused by all the current recommendations about what is healthy eating and what is not. We hope this book will remove some of the confusion. Menus have been planned according to Canada's Guidelines for Healthy Eating (*what* to eat), as well as the Good Health Eating Guide of the Canadian Diabetes Association (*how much* to eat and *when*). The Food Choice values used in planning each meal are shown on the next page. (For more information about the Food Choice System of meal planning, see page 123.) That's the beauty of *Choice Menus*. It takes the guesswork out of meal planning.

We believe that food is one of life's greatest pleasures and meal times can be high points in your day.

AN EXAMPLE MEAL PLAN

	1200 CALORIES*	1500 CALORIES*	1800 CALORIES*
Your Choice of Breakfast			
Mid-Morning			add 150-calorie snack
Your Choice of Lunch			
Mid-Afternoon			add 150-calorie snack
Your Choice of Dinner			
Evening		add **one** 300-calorie snack in evening OR **two** 150-calorie snacks (**one** during day and **one** in evening)	add 300-calorie snack

* when skim milk is used

Each BREAKFAST in this section provides about 340 calories* and is based on:

2 ☐ STARCHY CHOICES
1 ◪ FRUITS & VEGETABLES CHOICE
1 ◨ 2% MILK CHOICE
1 ▨ PROTEIN CHOICE
1 ▲ FATS & OILS CHOICE

*320 calories with skim milk

....

Each LUNCH in this section provides about 440 calories* and is based on:

2 ☐ STARCHY CHOICES
2 ◪ FRUITS & VEGETABLES CHOICES
1 ◨ 2% MILK CHOICE
2 ▨ PROTEIN CHOICES
1 ▲ FATS & OILS CHOICE
1 ▥ EXTRA VEGETABLES

*420 calories with skim milk

....

Each DINNER in this section provides about 500 calories* and is based on:

2 ☐ STARCHY CHOICES
2 ◪ FRUITS & VEGETABLES CHOICES
1 ◨ 2% MILK CHOICE
3 ▨ PROTEIN CHOICES
1 ▲ FATS & OILS CHOICE
1 ▥ EXTRA VEGETABLES

*480 calories with skim milk

....

SNACKS provide either 150 calories (with 20 to 25 grams carbohydrate)

OR 300 calories (with 35 to 40 grams carbohydrate)

High fibre muffins, always
at the top of the
breakfast hit parade
(page 61)

**Enjoy a hearty
lunch of old-fashioned
split pea soup**
(page 66)

Pasta and vegetable salad, a great hot-weather lunch for home or work *(page 70)*

Plan a snack to avoid that between-meal slump. See Snack Menus 1 to 32 for ideas.

A beef and vegetable stew
will be welcome at dinner
on a cold blustery day
(page 93)

**Special Occasions
call for special menus
*(For ideas see
page 107)***

A creamy molded dessert
with raspberry sauce, the
crowning touch to a
festive meal
(page 116)

Delicious, nutritious fruit, the perfect ending for any meal.

BREAKFAST

Your parents were right: in many ways breakfast *is* the most important meal in the day.

But, you say, I don't have time for breakfast. Is it really that important?

Yes, it is! Eating breakfast after a long overnight fast increases energy levels and helps prevent those mid-morning cravings that find you reaching for something high in calories (and high in fat, too). Eating breakfast also "primes the pump" that releases insulin into the bloodstream. This results in lower glucose levels before lunch and over the rest of the day as well. So, yes, it is important for you to eat breakfast to keep your weight and diabetes under control.

Breakfast is also the time to include cereals rich in the soluble and insoluble fibre so important to health. You really can't satisfy your fibre needs without eating a daily serving of a fibre-rich cereal. See the Introduction for further information on fibre.

Some days you simply don't have time for a sit-down breakfast. In that case, Menu #8, "Breakfast on the Run," may be right up your alley. Maybe quickly prepared Microwave Porridge for One *(page 52)* is your fast-start answer. Another approach is to take time on a weekend to prepare one of our breakfast recipes in quantity to store or freeze. Raisin Bran Buttermilk Muffins *(page 61)*, and Crunchy Breakfast Oats *(page 57)* are ideal recipes for making ahead and storing.

Maybe the real reason you don't eat breakfast is because you find it boring. Our menus and recipes contain the variety and interest necessary to make breakfast the outstanding meal of your day! We hope you will feel inspired to try them and find some favourites to enjoy again and again.

Don't say you can't *take* time for breakfast; *make* the time. It's important!

Fruit or Juice?

"Eat your fruit, don't drink it" is a good motto to follow. Fruit juices are a source of vitamins and minerals, but the valuable fibre has been lost during processing. Raw fruits contain the same vitamins, yet have insoluble and often soluble fibre as well. Since it takes more time to digest the fibre in raw fruit, the fruit's natural sugar is released more slowly than when you drink juice. This in turn results in a more gradual increase in blood glucose after a meal. And there is an additional benefit: you'll feel more satisfied after eating a piece of fruit than after drinking a glass of juice. If you do have a small glass of juice on occasion, sip it slowly with your meal.

With or Without

When it comes to having a beverage with a meal, different people have different preferences. Since each menu is planned to include milk, we have assumed that you will save some from your cereal to put in your tea or coffee. If a menu does not include cereal, the menu still allows enough milk for a cup of your favourite brew. If your preference is clear tea or black coffee, use all the milk on your cereal or add a spoonful of yogurt to your fruit. If you don't want to use milk or yogurt at all, discuss other ways to meet your calcium needs with your dietitian.

> 1 tbsp (15 mL) 1% milk adds 6 calories
> 1 tbsp (15 mL) 2% milk adds 8 calories
> 1 tbsp (15 mL) 10% cream adds 20 calories
> 1 tbsp (15 mL) 18% cream adds 28 calories
> Creamers in restaurants usually contain 1 tbsp (15 mL).

Multi-use Recipes

You'll find recipes in the breakfast chapter used at other meals. Rolled Oat Muesli *(page 59)* is a good example. It is served as cereal with fruit in the morning and as a dinner dessert. Multimix is another. It is used for breakfast Multimix Pancakes *(page 54)* and in Banana Muffins *(page 57)* as well as for Buttermilk Scones *(page 100)* and Multimix Tea Biscuits *(page 101)*. Planning ahead makes short work of food preparation.

BREAKFAST RECIPES INDEX

Kick-start your day with this cooked hot cereal, rich in soluble fibre.

½ cup	water	125 mL
¼ cup	quick cooking rolled oats	50 mL
¼ tsp	vanilla or maple extract	1 mL

• In microwavable serving bowl, combine water, rolled oats and vanilla extract. Microwave, uncovered, on High (100%) for 1½ to 2 minutes; stir once. Let stand for 1 to 2 minutes or until desired consistency. Stir and serve.
• For a thinner porridge, add 1 to 2 tbsp (15 to 25 mL) more water.

Makes 1 serving, ½ cup (125 mL).
PREPARATION: *under 5 minutes*
COOK: *1½ to 2 minutes*

For a double serving, use 1 cup (250 mL) water and ½ cup (125 mL) rolled oats.

Each serving: ½ cup (125 mL)
1 ☐ Starchy Choice
14 g carbohydrate, 3 g protein, 1 g fat, 2 g fibre, 79 kcal (330 kJ)

Stove-Top Porridge for the Family
• In saucepan, combine 1 cup (250 mL) rolled oats and 2 cups (500 mL) water. Cook on medium heat for 5 to 6 minutes; stir occasionally. Cover, remove from heat; stir in 1 tsp (5 mL) vanilla extract, let stand a few minutes before serving.

Makes 4 servings, 2 cups (500 mL).

Variations

CITRUS OATMEAL PORRIDGE
• Replace vanilla extract with ¼ tsp (1 mL) grated orange, lemon, mandarin orange or tangerine rind and a pinch of ground ginger. Cook as above.

Each serving: ½ cup (125 mL)
1 ☐ Starchy Choice
14 g carbohydrate, 3 g protein, 1 g fat, 2 g fibre, 79 kcal (330 kJ)

AUTUMN OATMEAL PORRIDGE
• Replace vanilla extract with 1 tbsp (15 mL) sunflower, pumpkin or sesame seeds. Cook as above.

Each serving: ½ cup (125 mL)
1 ☐ Starchy Choice 1 ▲ Fats & Oils Choice
15 g carbohydrate, 5 g protein, 6 g fat, 3 g fibre, 128 kcal (540 kJ)

RAISIN OATMEAL PORRIDGE
• Add 1 tbsp (15 mL) raisins and a pinch of ground cinnamon. Cook as above.

Each serving: ½ cup (125 mL)
1 ☐ Starchy Choice ½ ◨ Fruits & Vegetables Choice
22 g carbohydrate, 4 g protein, 1 g fat, 3 g fibre, 108 kcal (450 kJ)

Cereals provide a nutritious start to the day. For variety, try this combination of three popular whole grain cereals.

Dry Cereal Mix

1 cup	quick cooking rolled oats	250 mL
1 cup	oat bran	250 mL
1 cup	whole grain cereal*	250 mL

• Combine rolled oats, oat bran and whole grain cereal. Store in tightly sealed container.

Makes 3 cups (750 mL).
Each serving: ¼ cup (50 mL)

HOT MULTIGRAIN CEREAL FOR ONE

Microwave
• In microwavable serving bowl, combine ¼ cup (50 mL) cereal mix, ¾ cup (175 mL) water and dash maple or vanilla extract. Microwave, uncovered, on High (100%) for 2 minutes; stir. Microwave on Low (30%) for 3 minutes. Let stand for 2 minutes. Stir and serve.

Stove-Top
• In saucepan, combine ¼ cup (50 mL) cereal mix, ¾ cup (175 mL) water and dash maple or vanilla extract. Cook on medium-low heat for 3 to 5 minutes or until desired consistency; stir occasionally. Cover and remove from heat; let stand a few minutes. Stir and serve.

KITCHEN TIP

*Whole grain cereal comes by different names depending on where you live in Canada. Red River, Sunny Boy and Brex are examples.

Makes 1 serving, ¾ cup (175 mL).
PREPARATION: for dry mix, 5 minutes
COOK: for 1 serving, 3 to 5 minutes

1 serving as prepared
1 ☐ Starchy Choice
17 g carbohydrate, 4 g protein, 1 g fat, 3 g fibre, 80 kcal (330 kJ)

HOT MULTIGRAIN CEREAL FOR ONE WITH DRIED FRUIT

• Add 1 tsp (5 mL) raisins or chopped dried apples or apricots. Replace maple or vanilla extract with a pinch of ground cinnamon or nutmeg. Cook as above.

1 serving as prepared
1 ☐ Starchy Choice ½ ▟ Fruits & Vegetables Choice
19 g carbohydrate, 4 g protein, 1 g fat, 3 g fibre, 88 kcal (370 kJ)

KITCHEN TIP

To microwave more than one serving, choose a deeper bowl to prevent boiling over. A glass 2-cup (500 mL) measuring cup is appropriate.

MULTIMIX

Keep this handy mix stored in the refrigerator for fast preparation of pancakes, muffins, scones and tea biscuits.

3 cups	all purpose flour	750 mL
2 cups	whole wheat flour	500 mL
3 tbsp	baking powder	45 mL
1 cup	shortening	250 mL
	(about ½ pkg/454 g)	

• In large bowl, combine flours and baking powder. Cut in shortening with knives or a pastry blender until mixture resembles coarse crumbs or blend the mixture in a food processor bowl.
• Store in refrigerator in airtight container.

Makes about 8 cups (2 L).
PREPARATION: 10 minutes

• Stored in the refrigerator, Multimix keeps for two months. For other Multimix recipes, see pages 57, 100, 101.

MULTIMIX PANCAKES WITH BLUEBERRY SAUCE

Teamed with microwave-cooked fresh fruit sauce instead of syrup, these quick-fix pancakes are a very satisfying start to the day.

Pancakes

1½ cups	**Multimix**	375 mL
1 tsp	granulated sugar	5 mL
1 cup	skim milk	250 mL
1	egg, beaten	1
1 tsp	vanilla extract	5 mL
1 tsp	vegetable oil	5 mL

• In bowl, combine Multimix and sugar.
• In small bowl, combine milk, egg and vanilla extract. Pour into dry ingredients; stir just until dry ingredients are moistened.
• Heat nonstick skillet over medium heat until hot. Brush with oil to lightly grease. Pour batter, using ¼ cup (50 mL) measure, onto hot skillet. Cook 2 to 3 minutes or until bubbles form on surface and underside is golden brown. Turn pancakes and cook just until bottom is lightly browned.

Makes 4 servings, twelve 4-inch (10-cm) pancakes.
PREPARATION: 10 minutes
COOK: about 5 minutes each

Each serving: 3 pancakes
2 ☐ Starchy Choices
½ ☑ Protein Choices
2½ ▲ Fats & Oils Choices
29 g carbohydrate, 8 g protein, 14 g fat,
2 g fibre, 270 kcal (1130 kJ)

Blueberry Sauce

⅔ cup	water	150 mL
1 tbsp	granulated sugar	15 mL
1 tbsp	cornstarch	15 mL
1¼ cups	fresh or frozen blueberries	300 mL

• In 2-cup (500 mL) glass measure, combine water, sugar and cornstarch. Stir in blueberries. Microwave on High (100%) for 3 to 4 minutes or until slightly thickened and blueberries have softened; stir every 2 minutes.

Makes 1 cup (250 mL) sauce.
PREPARATION: 5 minutes
COOK: 3 to 4 minutes

Each serving: ¼ cup (50 mL)
1 ◪ Fruits & Vegetables Choice
11 g carbohydrate, 0 g protein, 0 g fat,
1 g fibre, 44 kcal (180 kJ)

Sauce Variations

SPICY BLUEBERRY

• Add a pinch each of ground cinnamon and nutmeg to cooked Blueberry Sauce.

CITRUS

• Add grated lemon or orange rind to cooked Blueberry Sauce.

KITCHEN TIP

Fruit sauces like this blueberry one are excellent served over frozen waffles, milk puddings and low-fat ice cream or frozen yogurt. *(See Lunch Menu #23.)*

Tasty, small-batch fresh fruit spreads require only a small amount of sugar, very short cooking time and no added pectin. They will keep in the refrigerator for about a month.

1	envelope unflavoured gelatin	1
⅓ cup	cold water	75 mL
3 cups	sliced strawberries **or**	750 mL
2½ cups	mashed strawberries	625 mL
2 tbsp	granulated sugar	25 mL
4 tsp	lemon juice	20 mL
1 tsp	grated lemon rind	5 mL

• In saucepan, sprinkle gelatin over water. Stir over low heat until gelatin is completely dissolved.
• Add strawberries, sugar, lemon juice and rind. Bring to a boil. Cover and cook for 5 minutes or until fruit is tender; stir occasionally.
• Spoon into sterilized jars; cool slightly. Refrigerate several hours or until set.
• Store in the refrigerator for up to 1 month or for 1 year in the freezer.

Makes 2 cups (500 mL).
PREPARATION: *10 minutes*
COOK: *about 5 minutes*

Fruit Spread Variations
Cooking times may differ with each fruit.

RASPBERRY

• Replace strawberries with 3 cups (750 mL) slightly crushed raspberries and lemon rind with orange rind.

PEACH AND PEAR

• Replace strawberries with 2 cups (500 mL) peeled and sliced peaches and 1 cup (250 mL) chopped pears, and lemon rind with ½ tsp (2 mL) ground nutmeg.

BLUEBERRY

• Replace strawberries with 3 cups (750 mL) lightly crushed fresh or frozen blueberries and add ½ tsp (2 mL) ground ginger.

Each serving: 1 tbsp (15 mL)
1 ✚✚ Extra
2 g carbohydrate, 0 g protein, 0 g fat, 0 g fibre, 10 kcal (40 kJ)

KITCHEN TIPS

• When fresh fruits are not available, these spreads may be made using unsweetened frozen fruits. Measure fruit while still slightly frozen.
• Each pouch of unflavoured gelatin contains 1 tbsp (15 mL). This amount of gelatin is sufficient to set 2 cups (500 mL) of liquid. If desired, smaller amounts of jam may be prepared using less gelatin.

ORANGE FRENCH TOAST WITH HONEY YOGURT SAUCE

Try this recipe for a leisurely weekend breakfast. Orange rind provides a different flavour; honey provides sweetness, and a little goes a long way.

French Toast

1/3 cup	low-fat milk	75 mL
1	egg, lightly beaten	1
1/2 tsp	grated orange rind	2 mL
1/4 tsp	salt	1 mL
1/4 tsp	vanilla extract	1 mL
2 slices	white or whole wheat bread	2 slices
1/2 tsp	margarine or butter	2 mL
	Ground nutmeg	

• In shallow pie plate, combine milk, egg, orange rind, salt and vanilla extract. Dip each bread slice into egg mixture, coating each side well.
• In large nonstick skillet, melt margarine over medium heat. Cook bread for 2 minutes each side or until golden brown. Serve sprinkled with nutmeg.

Oven Preparation
• Melt margarine on nonstick baking pan in 400°F (200°C) oven. Place dipped bread slices on pan. Bake for about 10 minutes per side. This makes a crisper French toast.

Makes 1 serving.
PREPARATION: *about 10 minutes*
COOK: *5 minutes*

Honey Yogurt Sauce

1/4 cup	low-fat plain yogurt	50 mL
1 tsp	liquid honey	5 mL

• In small bowl, combine yogurt and honey.

Makes 1/4 cup (50 mL).
PREPARATION: *5 minutes*

**Each serving: 2 slices
with 1/4 cup (50 mL) Honey Yogurt Sauce**

2 ☐ Starchy Choices
1 ◪ Fruits & Vegetables Choice
1/2 ◆ 2% Milk Choice
1 1/2 ◪ Protein Choices
1 ▲ Fats & Oils Choice

*44 g carbohydrate, 17 g protein, 11 g fat,
1 g fibre, 348 kcal (1460 kJ)*

Variation

. . . .
CINNAMON FRENCH TOAST

• Follow recipe above, replacing 1/2 tsp (2 mL) grated orange rind with 1/2 tsp (2 mL) ground cinnamon.

Each serving: 2 slices

2 ☐ Starchy Choices
1/2 ◆ 2% Milk Choice
1 ◪ Protein Choice
1 ▲ Fats & Oils Choice

*33 g carbohydrate, 14 g protein, 10 g fat,
1 g fibre, 288 kcal (1200 kJ)*

. . . .
KITCHEN TIP

Make extra French toast. Allow to cool completely before wrapping each slice separately for freezer.

CRUNCHY BREAKFAST OATS

More commonly referred to as granola. In this version, the fat and sugar, but not the fibre, have been reduced.

1½ cups	quick cooking rolled oats	375 mL
½ cup	natural bran	125 mL
¼ cup	wheat germ	50 mL
3 tbsp	chopped almonds	45 mL
2 tbsp	liquid honey	25 mL
2 tbsp	margarine or butter	25 mL
2 tbsp	water	25 mL
¼ cup	skim milk powder	50 mL
¼ cup	raisins	50 mL
¼ cup	unsweetened coconut	50 mL
¼ cup	sunflower seeds	50 mL
1 tsp	ground cinnamon	5 mL

• In large bowl, combine oats, bran, wheat germ and almonds.
• In saucepan, heat honey, margarine and water until hot. Stir into oat mixture. Spread on baking pan.
• Bake in 350°F (180°C) oven for 8 to 10 minutes or until lightly toasted; stir once. Let cool completely.
• Stir in skim milk powder, raisins, coconut, sunflower seeds and cinnamon. Store in tightly sealed container.

Makes 7 servings, 3½ cups (875 mL).
PREPARATION: 10 minutes
COOK: 8 to 10 minutes

Each serving: ½ cup (125 mL)

1 □ Starchy Choices
1 ◪ Fruits & Vegetables Choice
½ ◪ Protein Choice
2 ▲ Fats & Oils Choices

26 g carbohydrate, 8 g protein, 11 g fat, 5 g fibre, 240 kcal (1010 kJ)

BANANA MUFFINS

Warm Banana Muffins are wonderfully satisfying at breakfast. Or pack them as a snack with your lunch.

2 cups	**Multimix** *(see page 54)*	500 mL
2 tbsp	granulated sugar	25 mL
½ tsp	baking soda	2 mL
⅔ cup	mashed banana (1½ small)	150 mL
½ cup	buttermilk or sour milk*	125 mL
1	egg, beaten	1
1 tsp	vanilla extract	5 mL

• In medium bowl, combine Multimix, sugar and baking soda.
• In small bowl, stir together banana, buttermilk, egg and vanilla extract.
• Pour into dry ingredients; stir just until combined.
• Spoon into 12 nonstick or paper-lined medium muffin cups. Bake in 400°F (200°C) oven for about 20 minutes or until firm to the touch.

Makes 12 medium muffins.
PREPARATION: 10 minutes
COOK: 20 minutes

Each serving: 1 muffin (1/12 of recipe)

1 □ Starchy Choice
1 ▲ Fats & Oils Choice

17 g carbohydrate, 3 g protein, 6 g fat, 1 g fibre, 125 kcal (520 kJ)

KITCHEN TIP

*To sour milk, stir 1 tsp (5mL) lemon juice or vinegar into ½ cup (125 mL) milk; let stand for 5 minutes.

OATMEAL PANCAKES WITH MAPLE YOGURT SAUCE

Have your breakfast oatmeal in a pancake. Maple Yogurt Sauce tastes rich, but it's very low in calories.

Pancakes

1¼ cups	all purpose flour	300 mL
¾ cup	quick cooking rolled oats	175 mL
1 tbsp	granulated sugar	15 mL
½ tsp	ground cinnamon or nutmeg	2 mL
1½ cups	low-fat milk	375 mL
2	eggs, beaten	2
⅔ cup	unsweetened applesauce	150 mL
1 tbsp	vegetable oil	15 mL

• In medium bowl, combine flour, rolled oats, sugar and cinnamon.
• In second bowl, stir together milk, eggs and applesauce. Pour into dry ingredients; stir just until moistened.
• Heat oil in nonstick skillet over medium heat until hot. Pour batter with ¼-cup (50mL) measure into hot skillet; cook 2 to 3 minutes or until bubbles form on surface and underside is golden brown. Turn pancakes and cook just until bottom is lightly browned.

Makes 6 servings, eighteen 3-inch (7.5 cm) pancakes.
PREPARATION: *10 minutes*
COOK: *4 to 6 minutes*

Each serving: 3 pancakes

2 ☐ Starchy Choices
½ ▧ Fruits & Vegetables Choice
½ ▨ Protein Choice
1 ▲ Fats & Oils Choice

*37 g carbohydrate, 9 g protein, 6 g fat,
2 g fibre, 240 kcal (1000 kJ)*

Maple Yogurt Sauce

2 cups	low-fat plain yogurt	500 mL
4 tsp	granulated brown low-calorie sweetener*	20 mL
½ tsp	maple extract	2 mL
½ tsp	cinnamon	2 mL

• In a bowl, combine yogurt, sweetener, maple extract and cinnamon.
• Refrigerate until ready to serve.

*Liquid cyclamate sweetener (1¼ tsp/6 mL) can replace granulated in this recipe.

Makes 6 servings, 2 cups (500 mL) sauce.
PREPARATION: *5 minutes*

Each serving: ⅓ cup (75 mL) sauce

1 ◨ 2% Milk Choice

*6 g carbohydrate, 4 g protein, 1 g fat,
0 g fibre, 52 kcal (220 kJ)*

KITCHEN TIPS

• For best pancakes, don't overmix — they'll become tough. Allow batter to sit for a few minutes before cooking.
• Be sure to cook all the batter. Batter refrigerated for a day or two will yield thin, tough pancakes. Freeze extra cooked pancakes instead.

ROLLED OAT MUESLI

Swiss muesli has been a popular European breakfast item for generations. Served with fresh fruit, this unsweetened version is a very high source of fibre.

1 cup	quick cooking rolled oats	250 mL
1/3 cup	natural bran	75 mL
1/4 cup	unsweetened desiccated coconut	50 mL
3 tbsp	wheat germ	45 mL
3 tbsp	chopped almonds	45 mL
1 tsp	ground cinnnamon	5 mL

• In bowl, combine rolled oats, bran, coconut, wheat germ, almonds and cinnamon. Spread on large baking pan.
• Bake in 300°F (150°C) oven for about 20 minutes or until lightly toasted; stir occasionally. Let cool completely. Store in tightly sealed container.

Makes 6 servings, 2 cups (500mL).
PREPARATION: 10 minutes
COOK: 20 minutes

Each serving: 1/3 cup (75 mL)

1 ☐ Starchy Choice
1 ▲ Fats & Oils Choice

15 g carbohydrate, 5 g protein, 6 g fat, 3 g fibre, 119 kcal (500 kJ)

Variation

MUESLI BREAKFAST PARFAIT

1/2 cup	sliced fresh strawberries	125 mL
1/4 cup	low-fat plain yogurt	50 mL
1/4 cup	Rolled Oat Muesli	50 mL
1	whole strawberry or slice kiwifruit for optional garnish	1

• In parfait or sherbet glass, layer one-half strawberries, 2 tbsp (25 mL) yogurt and 2 tbsp (25 mL) muesli; repeat layers.
• Top with whole strawberry or slice kiwifruit, if using.

Makes 1 serving.
PREPARATION: 5 minutes

Each serving:

1/2 ☐ Starchy Choice
1/2 ▱ Fruits & Vegetables Choice
1/2 ◆ 2% Milk Choice
1/2 ▨ Protein Choice
1/2 ▲ Fats & Oils Choice

21 g carbohydrate, 7 g protein, 5 g fat, 4 g fibre, 150 kcal (630 kJ)

BREAKFAST EGG PITAS

Get your day off to a nutritious start with Mexican-inspired Breakfast Egg Pitas. The "heat" will depend on whether you choose mild, medium or hot salsa.

½ tsp	margarine or butter	2 mL
1	green onion, chopped	1
2	large mushrooms, sliced	2
4	eggs, beaten	4
2 tbsp	shredded part-skim mozzarella **or** light Cheddar cheese	25 mL
¼ tsp	dry mustard	1 mL
¼ tsp	dillweed	1 mL
Pinch	each salt and pepper	Pinch
2	6-inch (15 cm) whole wheat pita bread rounds, split in half	2
4	leaves lettuce	4
4 tsp	Mexican salsa	20 mL

• In a small nonstick skillet, melt margarine on medium heat. Add onion and mushrooms and cook for 2 minutes.
• Combine eggs, cheese and seasonings. Add to skillet. Cook, stirring occasionally, for 3 to 4 minutes or until eggs are set and cheese is melted.
• Line pita halves with lettuce leaves. Divide cooked egg among four pita halves. Top each pita with 1 tsp (5 mL) salsa.

Makes 4 servings.
PREPARATION: 10 minutes
COOK: about 5 minutes

Each serving: ¼ of recipe

1 ☐ Starchy Choice
1 ☑ Protein Choice
1 ▲ Fats & Oils Choice

19 g carbohydrate, 11 g protein, 7 g fat, 3 g fibre, 178 kcal (740 kJ)

EGGS FLORENTINE

This colourful egg dish is a microwave version of an old classic. Serve it to friends for weekend brunch.

1	pkg (300 g) frozen chopped spinach, thawed and well drained	1
1	large tomato, chopped	1
1	green onion, chopped	1
6	eggs	6
2 tbsp	grated Parmesan cheese	25 mL
6	English muffins, halved and toasted	6

• In small microwavable bowl, combine spinach, tomato and onion. Cover and microwave on High (100%) for 3 minutes. Divide mixture among six individual custard cups or microwavable ramekins.
• Break one egg into each dish; pierce yolk with fork. Sprinkle evenly with Parmesan cheese. Microwave covered on Medium-High (70%) for 7 to 9 minutes, or until eggs are cooked as desired.
• Using a rubber spatula, slide cooked egg mixture out of baking dish onto toasted English muffin half. Serve with second muffin half.

Makes 6 servings.
PREPARATION: 15 minutes
COOK: 6 servings, 7 to 9 minutes

---

1 serving: ⅙ of recipe

2 ☐ Starchy Choices
1½ ☑ Protein Choices
½ ▲ Fats & Oils Choice

31 g carbohydrate, 14 g protein, 7 g fat, 2 g fibre, 241 kcal (1010 kJ)

KITCHEN TIP

If you are microwaving only one serving at a time, microwave on Medium-High (70%) for 1½ to 2 minutes.

RAISIN BRAN BUTTERMILK MUFFINS

High-fibre muffins are always at the top of the breakfast hit parade. This is an extremely reliable recipe with several variations.

1½ cups	buttermilk*	375 mL
1½ cups	high fibre wheat bran cereal**	375 mL
1	egg, beaten	1
3 tbsp	vegetable oil	45 mL
1 tsp	vanilla extract	5 mL
1 cup	whole wheat flour	250 mL
2 tbsp	granulated sugar	25 mL
2 tsp	baking powder	10 mL
½ tsp	baking soda	2 mL
2 tbsp	raisins, chopped	25 mL

• In bowl, stir buttermilk into cereal; let stand for 5 minutes or until cereal is softened. Beat in egg, oil and vanilla extract.
• In large bowl, combine flour, sugar, baking powder, baking soda and raisins. Add buttermilk mixture; stir just until combined.
• Spoon into 12 nonstick or paper-lined medium muffin cups. Bake in 400°F (200°C) oven for about 20 minutes or until firm to the touch.

Makes 12 medium muffins.
PREPARATION: 15 minutes
COOK: 20 minutes

Muffin Variations

Replace raisins with
• 2 tbsp (25 mL) chopped dried apricots (4 halves); **or**
• ½ cup (125 mL) fresh or frozen blueberries and ½ tsp (2 mL) ground cinnamon; **or**
• ½ cup (125 mL) chopped apple (½ medium apple) and ½ tsp (2 mL) ground nutmeg.

Each serving: 1 muffin (¹⁄₁₂ of recipe)

1 ☐ Starchy Choice
1 ▲ Fats & Oils Choice

*20 g carbohydrate, 4 g protein, 5 g fat,
4 g fibre, 123 kcal (510 kJ)*

KITCHEN TIPS

*If you don't have buttermilk, stir 4 tsp (20 mL) vinegar or lemon juice into 1½ cups (375 mL) milk; let stand 5 minutes.
**Examples of high fibre wheat bran cereals are All-Bran and 100% Bran Cereal.

SINGLE-SERVE HAM 'N' CHEESE EGGS

A small amount of ham added to an egg goes a long way. This recipe tastes great any time of day!

2 tbsp	finely chopped ham	25 mL
1 tbsp	chopped celery	15 mL
1 tbsp	chopped onion	15 mL
½ tsp	margarine or butter	2 mL
1	egg, beaten	1
Pinch	each pepper and paprika	Pinch
1 tbsp	shredded mozzarella cheese	15 mL
½	English muffin, toasted **or**	½
1	slice whole wheat toast	1

• In small custard cup, combine ham, celery, onion and margarine. Microwave, uncovered, on High (100%) for 2 minutes.
• Stir in egg and seasonings. Microwave on Medium-High (70%) for 40 to 50 seconds; stir once.
• Top with shredded cheese; let stand for about 1 minute to allow cheese to melt.
• Serve on a toasted English muffin half or whole wheat toast.

Makes 1 serving
PREPARATION: 5 minutes
COOK: about 3 minutes

Each serving: 1 egg on ½ English muffin

1 ☐ Starchy Choice
1½ ⊘ Protein Choices
1 ▲ Fats & Oils Choice

*15 g carbohydrate, 14 g protein, 10 g fat,
1 g fibre, 208 kcal (870 kJ)*

WHOLE WHEAT ENGLISH MUFFINS

You'll love the taste of your own homemade, hot-off-the-griddle English muffins. You may never purchase store-bought ones again! Quick rising instant yeast makes preparation easy.

2½ cups	all purpose flour, divided	625 mL
1 cup	whole wheat flour	250 mL
2 tbsp	brown sugar	25 mL
1	envelope quick-rise instant yeast	1
½ tsp	salt	2 mL
1¼ cups	low-fat milk	300 mL
2 tbsp	margarine or butter	25 mL
2 tsp	cornmeal, divided (optional)	10 mL
1 tsp	vegetable oil	5 mL

• In large bowl, combine 1½ cups (375 mL) all purpose flour, whole wheat flour, sugar, yeast and salt.

• Heat milk and margarine until hot to touch (125°F/50°C). Stir into flour mixture. Mix in enough of the remaining 1 cup (250 mL) all purpose flour to make a soft dough that does not stick to bowl. Let rest for 5 minutes.

• Knead dough on lightly floured surface for about 8 minutes or until smooth. Cover; let rest 10 minutes.

• Divide dough into 12 equal pieces; shape each into a smooth ball. Roll each ball into 3-inch (7.5 cm) circle. Sprinkle each of two baking pans with ½ tsp (2 mL) cornmeal, if using. Transfer muffins to pans. Brush muffin tops with water; sprinkle muffins with remaining 1 tsp (5 mL) cornmeal. Cover; let rise in warm, draft-free place for 40 minutes or until doubled in size.

• Heat a nonstick skillet or griddle over medium heat until hot. Brush lightly with oil. Place muffins in skillet; cook first side for 3 minutes or until browned. Turn muffins and cook for 3 minutes. Remove to wire rack to cool.

Makes 12 muffins.
PREPARATION: about 60 minutes
COOK: 6 minutes

Each serving:1 muffin (¹⁄₁₂ of recipe)

2 ☐ Starchy Choices
1 ▲ Fats & Oils Choice

33 g carbohydrate, 6 g protein, 3 g fat, 2 g fibre, 183 kcal (770 kJ)

KITCHEN TIPS

• To serve, split muffins in half with a fork rather than with a knife; toast if desired. Leftovers are best frozen to retain their freshness.
• The rest time is important in this recipe. It allows the dough to relax, thus making it much easier to roll out.

LUNCH

If you feel that lunch is a ho-hum, boring meal—another bowl of soup, sandwich or salad—this section is for you. These Lunch Menus and recipes provide variety and interest, yet remain easy and quick to prepare.

Our menus include two types of mid-day meals: those eaten at home and those eaten away from home, either as "brown bag" lunches or as restaurant meals.

At-Home Lunches

SOUPS: We all realize now, more than ever, the superb health benefits of foods containing fibre. Since legumes and lentils provide one of our richest sources of soluble fibre, we include them in several hearty soups: Curried Vegetable and Split Pea Soup *(page 73)* and Lentil Vegetable Soup *(page 72)*. These recipes make enough for more than one meal, so pack them in single-serve amounts, label well and freeze for future lunches.

It is important to remove as much fat as possible from soups containing meat. Trim visible fat from the meat before cooking. Chill the cooked soup, then simply skim off the fat—and the calories.

If you have high blood pressure or have been advised to limit salt, use homemade broths in soups instead of bouillon cubes or powders, or look for those with lower salt content. *(See Tip on page 73.)*

SANDWICHES: Too bad—the mayonnaise, butter and margarine we use to moisten sandwiches are loaded with fat and calories. Fillings in sandwiches often have more calories than the bread! That's why our menus give the exact weight in grams for meats and cheeses and measured amounts of other fillings. Eating larger amounts can add many extra calories to a meal. Attendants at deli meat and cheese counters are very willing to weigh out just the amount you need. Better still, buy a diet scale for your own use.

There are many satisfying lower-calorie substitutes for the mayonnaise, butter and margarine we commonly use. Mustard adds great flavour to sliced meat in a sandwich. What about using chopped and shredded raw vegetables for flavour and moisture in fillings? Or thin mayonnaise with some plain yogurt for Tuna Sandwich Filling *(page 67)*. Fresh herbs such as dill and parsley, or dried herbs and lemon juice, also add interesting flavour and moisture.

SALADS: Dressing on a salad can add an incredible amount of fat calories. Try eating a salad without any dressing. You will find the fresh flavour of the salad greens really delivers. If this doesn't appeal to you, check out some of the salad recipes in this section. Two come to mind—the Pasta Primavera Salad *(page 70)* with its tangy tomato juice and red wine vinegar dressing, and the Cabbage Waldorf Salad *(page 72)* with a yogurt and light mayonnaise dressing. Use the bottled light dressings suggested in our menus when time is short.

DESSERTS: Our goal in this section is to provide simple, mainly no-cook desserts. That's why you will find fruit frequently included in Lunch Menus. If you are using the 1200-calorie menu plan, you may choose to save dessert for a snack later on, especially if lunch is a bit bigger than you are used to eating.

Lunches Away From Home

RESTAURANT MEALS: Salads are important to include in your daily meals and can be a wise choice in restaurants. The biggest problem with restaurant or deli salads is the amount of high-fat dressing served on them. Learn to say, "May I have the dressing on the side, please." This way, *you* decide how much dressing you eat.

LUNCHES CARRIED TO WORK: The "brown bag" lunch you carry with you can be a meal you look forward to—a pleasant change from restaurant meals. Lunches from home help control both your weight and your budget. Salad recipes such as Totable Lentil Apple Salad *(page 68)* with lots of crunchy vegetables are perfect to take in a small container for desk-top eating. Lunch Menus #4 and #8 provide portable sandwich lunches.

SOUP 'N' SANDWICH IN A BOWL

This is a novel way to eat your soup and sandwich at the same time.

1	can (28 oz/796 mL) tomatoes, undrained	1
1	can (10 oz/284 mL) tomato soup	1
2/3 cup	water	150 mL
1 tsp	dried basil	5 mL
1/4 tsp	garlic powder	1 mL
1/4 tsp	pepper	1 mL
5	slices whole wheat bread	5
1/2 cup	shredded light Cheddar cheese	125 mL
1	green onion, chopped	1

• Chop whole tomatoes. In 8-cup (2 L) microwavable casserole, combine tomatoes with juice, tomato soup, water and seasonings. Cover and microwave on High (100%) for about 9 minutes or until soup is hot.
• Toast bread; cut each slice into cubes.
• Spoon 1 cup (250 mL) soup into each of five bowls. Top each bowl with cubes from 1 slice of toast. Sprinkle each with about 2 tbsp (25 mL) cheese and some chopped green onion. Microwave for a few seconds until cheese melts.

Makes 5 servings, 5 cups (1.25 L).
PREPARATION: 15 minutes
COOK: 9 minutes

Each serving: 1 cup (250 mL)

1 ☐ Starchy Choice
1 ◪ Fruits & Vegetables Choice
1 ◪ Protein Choice

30 g carbohydrate, 9 g protein, 4 g fat, 5 g fibre, 179 kcal (750 kJ)

OLD-FASHIONED HAM AND SPLIT PEA SOUP

Savoury and satisfying pea soup contains high amounts of soluble fibre.

10 cups	water	2.5 L
2 lb	lean smoked ham shank	1 kg
2 1/4 cups	split green peas (450 g pkg)	550 mL
1 1/2 cups	chopped carrot (2 medium)	375 mL
1 cup	chopped celery	250 mL
1/3 cup	dry onion soup mix (35 g pkg)	75 mL
2	bay leaves	2

• In large saucepan, combine water, ham shank, peas, carrots, celery, soup mix and bay leaves. Cover and cook for 3 to 4 hours or until peas are soft and meat is tender; stir occasionally.
• Remove bay leaves and discard. Remove ham shank; allow to cool before removing meat from bone. Discard bone, rind and all visible fat. Chop 2 cups (500 mL) meat;* return to soup and reheat, if necessary.

Makes 12 servings, 12 cups (3 L).
PREPARATION: 20 minutes
COOK: 3 to 4 hours

Each serving: 1 cup (250 mL)

1 ☐ Starchy Choice
1/2 ◪ Fruits & Vegetables Choice
1 1/2 ◪ Protein Choices

26 g carbohydrate, 14 g protein, 2 g fat, 6 g fibre, 172 kcal (720 kJ)

KITCHEN TIP

*Use leftover meat in a sandwich filling.

TUNA SANDWICH FILLING

Most of us have a favourite sandwich filling. This may easily be tops on your list.

1	can (6½ oz/184 g) water-packed chunk white tuna, drained	1
2 tbsp	low-fat plain yogurt	25 mL
2 tbsp	light mayonnaise	25 mL
1 tbsp	horseradish	15 mL
2 tsp	chopped parsley	10 mL
Pinch	freshly ground pepper	Pinch

• In bowl, flake tuna. Combine with yogurt, mayonnaise, horseradish, parsley and pepper. Cover and refrigerate for up to one day.

Makes 4 servings, 1 cup (250 mL).
PREPARATION: 10 minutes
CHILL: up to 1 day

Each serving: ¼ cup (50 mL) filling

1½ ⊘ Protein Choices
1 ⊡⊡ Extra

*2 g carbohydrate, 10 g protein, 3 g fat,
0 g fibre, 76 kcal (320 kJ)*

KITCHEN TIP

Add extra crunch to sandwiches with alfalfa sprouts or pepper cress. Look for them at the produce counter on your next visit to the grocery store.

KITCHEN TIP

*The bread to use is the long thin French bread stick, known as baguette, which is approximately 2 x 3½ -inches (5 x 9 cm) in diameter and each loaf weighs about 300 g.

CHEESE-FILLED FRENCH TOAST SANDWICHES

Enjoy this recipe at brunch as well as lunchtime. Prepare and fill the sandwiches ahead. Then dip in egg mixture just before cooking.

2 tbsp	light cream cheese	25 mL
2 tbsp	**Fruit Spread** (*page 55*)	25 mL
8	slices (½-inch/1 cm thick) French bread stick (baguette)*	8
1	egg	1
¼ cup	skim milk	50 mL
½ tsp	vanilla extract	2 mL
1 tsp	margarine or butter	5 mL
	Ground cinnamon	

Stove-Top
• In bowl, combine cream cheese and fruit spread. Spread mixture evenly over 4 bread slices; top with remaining 4 slices.
• In shallow pie plate, beat egg, milk and vanilla. Dip each sandwich into egg mixture, coating both sides well.
• In large nonstick skillet, melt margarine over medium heat. Cook sandwiches for 3 minutes; turn and cook for 2 minutes or until golden brown. Sprinkle with cinnamon.

Oven Preparation
• Melt margarine on non-stick baking pan in 400°F (200°C) oven. Place dipped sandwiches on pan; bake for about 5 minutes per side. This makes a crisper sandwich.

Makes 2 servings.
PREPARATION: 10 minutes
COOK: 5 minutes

Each serving: 2 sandwiches.

2 ☐ Starchy Choices
1 ⊘ Protein Choice
1 ▲ Fats & Oils Choice

*27 g carbohydrate, 9 g protein, 10 g fat,
1 g fibre, 235 kcal (980 kJ)*

SEAFOOD CHOWDER

Hearty, yet low in calories, this delicious chowder chases away chilly days. Choose low-fat fish such as cod, haddock, halibut or turbot.

1 tbsp	margarine or butter	15 mL
½ cup	chopped onion (1 small)	125 mL
1 tbsp	all purpose flour	15 mL
2½ cups	low-fat milk	625 mL
1 cup	sliced celery	250 mL
1 cup	sliced carrot (2 medium)	250 mL
1⅔ cups	cubed potato (2 medium)	400 mL
½ tsp	salt	2 mL
½ tsp	dried thyme	2 mL
¼ tsp	pepper	1 mL
¾ lb	fish fillets	375 g
	(cod, turbot, haddock, halibut)	
	Chopped parsley	

• In large saucepan melt margarine on medium heat. Add onion and cook for 5 minutes or until onion is tender. Add flour; cook and stir for 2 minutes. Gradually stir in milk and bring slowly to a boil.
• Add celery, carrot, potato and seasonings. Cover and cook over low heat for about 20 minutes or until vegetables are tender.
• Cut fish into large pieces; add to soup. Cook for 5 minutes or until fish flakes easily with a fork.
• Sprinkle with chopped parsley and serve.

Makes 7 servings, 7 cups (1.75 L).
PREPARATION: 15 minutes
COOK: about 30 minutes

Each serving: 1 cup (250 mL)

½ ▢ Starchy Choice
1 ◆ 2% Milk Choice
1 ▨ Protein Choice

*16g carbohydrate, 14 g protein, 4 g fat,
2 g fibre, 155 kcal (650 kJ)*

TOTABLE LENTIL APPLE SALAD

Take this excellent salad on a picnic or to the office. Lentils are truly one of nature's high-fibre foods.

1 cup	unpeeled chopped apple	250 mL
	(1 medium)	
1 tbsp	lemon juice	15 mL
1	can (19 oz/540 mL) lentils **or**	1
1¾ cups	cooked lentils*	425 mL
1 cup	chopped celery	250 mL
1	green onion, chopped	1
¼ cup	light mayonnaise	50 mL
¼ cup	low-fat plain yogurt	50 mL
Pinch	freshly ground pepper	Pinch
	Lettuce leaves	

• In bowl, combine apple with lemon juice.
• Drain and wash canned lentils. Add lentils, celery and green onion to bowl. Stir in mayonnaise, yogurt and pepper.
• Cover and refrigerate for at least 30 minutes so flavours develop. Serve on lettuce leaves.
* To cook dry lentils: Wash lentils thoroughly; drain well. Cover and cook in twice as much water as lentils for about 15 minutes for salads; 30 minutes for vegetable and main dish recipes; 45 minutes for soups and purées.

Makes 4 servings, 4 cups (1 L).
PREPARATION: 15 minutes
CHILL: 30 minutes or longer

Each serving: 1 cup (250 mL)

1 ▢ Starchy Choice
½ ▨ Fruits & Vegetables Choice
1 ▨ Protein Choice
½ ▲ Fats & Oils Choice

*25 g carbohydrate, 9 g protein, 5 g fat,
4 g fibre, 178 kcal (740 kJ)*

LENTIL FACTS

• contain slowly digesting starch
• excellent source of soluble fibre
• low in fat and cholesterol
• high in vegetable protein,
• rich in B vitamins (thiamine and riboflavin)
• good source of iron

MICROWAVE SCRAMBLED EGG

Eggs cooked in the microwave oven are a "fast food" at lunch or breakfast.

½ tsp	margarine or butter	2 mL
1	egg	1
1 tbsp	water or milk	15 mL

• Melt margarine on High (100%) in large microwavable bowl. Stir in eggs and water. Cover with plastic wrap. Microwave on Medium-High (70%) for about 50 seconds. Stir twice during cooking. Let stand for about 30 seconds before serving.

Makes 1 serving.
PREPARATION: *under 5 minutes*
COOK: *about 50 seconds*

Variation

SEASONED SCRAMBLED EGG

• Vary flavours by adding seasonings such as dried basil or oregano; pinch dry mustard or ground nutmeg; celery or caraway seeds.

Each serving: 1 egg
1 ☑ Protein Choice
1 ▲ Fats & Oils Choice
1 g carbohydrate, 6 g protein, 7 g fat, 0 g fibre, 92 kcal (380 kJ)

For additional servings, increase cooking time according to how many eggs are being prepared. Follow chart below.

2 eggs	2 tbsp (25 mL) water or milk 1 tsp (5 mL) margarine or butter Cook for about 1½ to 1¾ minutes
4 eggs	¼ cup (50 mL) water or milk 2 tsp (10 mL) margarine or butter Cook for 2½ to 3 minutes
6 eggs	⅓ cup (75 mL) water or milk 1 tbsp (15 mL) margarine or butter Cook for 3 to 3½ minutes

SPRING RHUBARB SAUCE

The first stalks of rhubarb signal spring's arrival. Add a little sugar and some sweetener after cooking this speedy lunch dessert.

4 cups	sliced rhubarb (8 thin stalks)	2 L
½ cup	water	125 mL
2 tsp	grated orange rind	10 mL
¼ cup	granulated white low-calorie sweetener*	50 mL
1 tbsp	granulated sugar	15 mL

Stove-Top
• In saucepan, cook rhubarb, water and orange rind over medium heat for 5 minutes or until rhubarb is tender. Remove from heat; stir in sweetener and sugar.

Microwave
• Combine rhubarb, water and orange rind in microwavable casserole. Cover and microwave on High (100%) for 3 to 5 minutes; stir once. Stir in sweetener and sugar.

Makes 5 servings, 2½ cups (625 mL).
PREPARATION: *10 minutes*
COOK: *about 5 minutes*

Each serving: ½ cup (125 mL)
½ ☑ Fruits & Vegetables Choice
8 g carbohydrate, 1 g protein, 0 g fat, 2 g fibre, 33 kcal (140 kJ)

KITCHEN TIPS

• Since rhubarb freezes well, wash, chop and bag in amounts suitable for this recipe.
• *Liquid cyclamate sweetener can replace granulated sweetener—use 1 tbsp (15 mL)—in this recipe.

PASTA PRIMAVERA SALAD

Choose this salad as a great hot-weather lunch for home or work. Pasta is an excellent example of a slowly digested complex carbohydrate food.

Salad

1 cup	uncooked fusilli pasta	250 mL
1 cup	broccoli florets	250 mL
1 cup	diced part-skim mozzarella cheese	250 mL
1	firm medium tomato, chopped **or**	1
¼ cup	chopped red pepper	50 mL
1	green onion, chopped	1
	Lettuce leaves	

Tomato Vinegar Dressing

½ cup	tomato juice	125 mL
2 tbsp	red wine vinegar	25 mL
1 tbsp	olive oil	15 mL
1	small clove garlic, minced	1
¼ tsp	salt	1 mL
Pinch	coarsely ground pepper	Pinch

• In large amount of boiling water, cook pasta according to package directions, until al dente (tender but firm). Drain well and cool.
• Steam broccoli for 5 minutes or until tender-crisp. Chill in cold water; drain well.
• In large bowl, combine broccoli, pasta, cheese, tomato and onion.
• In measuring cup, whisk together tomato juice, vinegar, oil, garlic and salt and pepper. Pour half the dressing over pasta mixture; toss gently. Refrigerate remaining dressing for a second salad.
• Cover salad and refrigerate for at least 30 minutes so flavours develop. Serve on lettuce leaves.

Makes 4 servings, about 4 cups (1 L).
PREPARATION: 15 minutes
COOK: 10 minutes
CHILL: at least 30 minutes

Each serving: 1 cup (250 mL)

1 ☐ Starchy Choice
1½ ☑ Protein Choice
1 ▲ Fats & Oils Choice

*19 g carbohydrate, 13 g protein, 10 g fat,
2 g fibre, 212 kcal (890 kJ)*

BAKED BEAN SOUP

When time is limited, prepare this vegetarian recipe for a fast, simple and nutritious lunch.

1	can (19 oz/540 mL) tomatoes, undrained	1
1	can (14 oz/398 mL) vegetarian beans in tomato sauce	1
1 cup	water	250 mL
¼ cup	chopped onion	50 mL
½ tsp	dried oregano	2 mL
¼ tsp	dry mustard	1 mL
½ cup	shredded part-skim mozzarella cheese	125 mL

• Chop whole canned tomatoes. In medium saucepan, combine tomatoes, beans, water, onion and seasonings. Cover and cook on medium heat for 15 minutes or until hot and onion is tender.
• Sprinkle each serving with 2 tbsp (25 mL) cheese.

Makes 4 servings, 5 cups (1.25 L).
PREPARATION: 10 minutes
COOK: 15 minutes

Each serving: 1¼ cups (300 mL)

1 ☐ Starchy Choice
½ ☑ Fruits & Vegetables Choice
1 ⊘ Protein Choice

*29 g carbohydrate, 10 g protein, 3 g fat,
10 g fibre, 171 kcal (720 kJ)*

KITCHEN TIPS

• The extra tomato dressing is wonderful for a tossed green salad.
• Double this recipe to take for a pot-luck supper, and then all the Tomato Vinegar Dressing will be used.

HEARTY VEGETABLE BEEF SALAD

This complete salad-in-a-dish uses many vegetables and is a great use for cooked roast beef.

1 cup	cooked corn kernels	250 mL
½ lb	cooked roast beef,* cut into slivers	250 g
1½ cups	sliced celery	375 mL
1 cup	sliced mushrooms	250 mL
½ cup	thinly sliced carrot	125 mL
½ cup	chopped red pepper	125 mL
½ cup	chopped green pepper	125 mL
1	small zucchini, cubed	1
½	small onion, chopped	½
½ cup	**Herb Vinaigrette Dressing**	125 mL
	(*page 81*)	

• In bowl, combine corn, beef, celery, mushrooms, carrot, red and green pepper, zucchini and onion. Toss with prepared dressing.
• Cover and refrigerate for at least 30 minutes so flavours develop.

Makes 6 servings, 6 cups (1.5 L).
PREPARATION: *20 minutes*
CHILL: *30 minutes or longer*

Each serving: 1 cup (250 mL)

1 ◪ Fruits & Vegetables Choice
2 ◪ Protein Choices
½ ◪ Fats & Oils Choice
1 ◪ Extra Vegetables

*13 g carbohydrate, 14 g protein, 7 g fat,
2 g fibre, 160 kcal (670 kJ)*

KITCHEN TIPS

• If you have leftover corn on the cob, remove it from the cob to use in this salad. Or use canned or frozen corn kernels.
• *When shopping at the deli, buy lean roast beef for this salad or use leftover from a roast. For leftover roast beef, measure about 2 cups (500 mL) slivered meat.

LUNCHEON MACARONI AND CHEDDAR CHEESE

Good old "mac 'n' cheese" has lots of flavour, but in this version fewer calories from fat!

1 tsp	margarine or butter	5 mL
2 tbsp	finely chopped onion	25 mL
1	small clove garlic, minced	1
2 tbsp	all purpose flour	25 mL
2 cups	low-fat milk	500 mL
½ tsp	prepared **or** dry mustard	2 mL
¼ tsp	salt	1 mL
Dash	hot pepper sauce **or** paprika	Dash
1½ cups	shredded light Cheddar cheese	375 mL
1¼ cups	elbow macaroni	300 mL

• In medium saucepan, melt margarine over low heat. Cook onion and garlic in margarine for 5 minutes; do not brown.
• Whisk together flour, milk and seasonings; gradually stir into onion. Cook over medium heat until mixture is smooth and thickened, stirring constantly. Add cheese; stir until melted.
• In large amount of boiling water, cook macaroni according to package directions until al dente (tender but firm). Drain macaroni; add cheese sauce, toss well to combine.

Makes 4 servings, 4 cups (1 L).
PREPARATION: *10 minutes*
COOK: *15 minutes*

Each serving: 1 cup (250 mL)

2 ◻ Starchy Choices
1 ◪ 2% Milk Choice
2 ◪ Protein Choice
1 ◪ Fats & Oils Choice

*40 g carbohydrate, 22 g protein, 12 g fat,
1 g fibre, 361 kcal (1510 kJ)*

KITCHEN TIP

Freeze any remaining macaroni and cheese, in 1 cup (250 mL) amounts (*see Lunch Menu #29*).

Take a dressed-up cabbage salad to lunch! It's a great brown bag treat.

2 cups	coarsely shredded cabbage	500 mL
½ cup	sliced celery	125 mL
2 tbsp	each: finely chopped raisins and walnuts	25 mL
¼ cup	low-fat plain yogurt	50 mL
2 tbsp	light mayonnaise	25 mL
½ tsp	lemon juice	2 mL
	Salt and pepper to taste	
2	medium apples, cored and chopped	2

• In medium bowl, combine cabbage, celery, raisins and walnuts.
• Whisk together yogurt, mayonnaise and lemon juice; stir into cabbage mixture. Season to taste with salt and pepper.
• Cover and refrigerate for at least 30 minutes so flavours develop.
• Stir in apple at serving time.

Makes 4 servings, 5 cups (1.25 L).
PREPARATION: 15 minutes
CHILL: 30 minutes or longer

Each serving: 1¼ cups (300 mL)

2 ◪ Fruits & Vegetables Choices
1 ▲ Fats & Oils Choice

*19 g carbohydrate, 2 g protein, 5 g fat,
3 g fibre, 118 kcal (490 kJ)*

Variation

LETTUCE WALDORF SALAD

• Replace cabbage with shredded lettuce for a change.

Each serving: 1¼ cups (300 mL)

1½ ◪ Fruits & Vegetables Choices
1 ▲ Fats & Oils Choice

*18 g carbohydrate, 2 g protein, 5 g fat,
2 g fibre, 113 kcal (470 kJ)*

We prefer using red lentils for this recipe since they cook quickly. This large recipe allows you to stock the freezer for many lunches to come.

1 tbsp	vegetable oil	15 mL
5 cups	shredded cabbage	1.25 L
2 cups	shredded carrot (2)	500 mL
1 cup	chopped onion (1 large)	250 mL
3 cups	cubed turnip or rutabaga	750 mL
2 cups	chopped celery	500 mL
1 cup	red lentils, washed	250 mL
2	large cloves garlic, minced	2
2	bay leaves	2
1 tsp	dried marjoram	5 mL
½ to 1 tsp	chili powder	2 to 5 mL
8 cups	beef broth	2 L
⅓ cup	tomato paste	75 mL
	Salt and pepper to taste	
	Low-fat plain yogurt	

• In large pot, heat oil on medium-low heat; add cabbage, carrot and onion and cook for 15 minutes; stir occasionally.
• Add turnip, celery, lentils, garlic, seasonings, beef broth and tomato paste. Cover and cook for about 1½ hours or until vegetables and lentils are tender; stir occasionally. Taste and add salt and pepper as desired.
• Top each serving with 1 tbsp (15 mL) yogurt.

Makes 17 servings, 17 cups (4.25 L).
PREPARATION: 30 minutes
COOK: 1¾ hours

Each serving: 1 cup (250 mL)

1 ◪ Fruits & Vegetables Choice
1 ◪ Protein Choice

*14 g carbohydrate, 6 g protein, 2 g fat,
3 g fibre, 88 kcal (370 kJ)*

CURRIED VEGETABLE AND SPLIT PEA SOUP

This wonderful wintertime soup tantalizes the taste buds with its subtle aromas and flavours. Since a large quantity of cooked soup is produced, freeze it in single-serving sizes.

1 tbsp	vegetable oil	15 mL
1 cup	chopped onion (1 medium)	250 mL
2	cloves garlic, minced	2
2 tbsp	minced gingerroot **or**	25 mL
1 tsp	ground ginger	5 mL
2	cinnamon sticks	2
2	bay leaves	2
1 tbsp	curry powder	15 mL
9 cups	chicken broth	2.25 L
2 cups	dried yellow split peas	500 mL
1½ cups	chopped carrot (3 medium)	375 mL
2 cups	chopped celery	500 mL
2 cups	finely chopped cauliflower	500 mL
2 tbsp	tomato paste	25 mL
	Salt and pepper	

• In large heavy saucepan, heat oil over medium heat. Add onion, garlic, gingerroot, cinnamon sticks and bay leaves. Cover and cook for 5 minutes or until vegetables are tender. Stir in curry powder and cook for 2 minutes.
• Add chicken broth and split peas. Cover and simmer for 45 minutes or until peas are almost tender.
• Add carrot, celery, cauliflower and tomato paste. Cover and simmer for 20 minutes or until peas and vegetables are tender. Season to taste with salt and pepper. Remove cinnamon sticks and bay leaves and discard.

Makes 12 servings, 12 cups (3 L).
PREPARATION: 20 minutes
COOK: 1 hour and 10 minutes

Each serving:1 cup (250 mL)

1 ☐ Starchy Choice
½ ☑ Fruits & Vegetables Choice
1½ ☑ Protein Choices

*26 g carbohydrate, 13 g protein, 3 g fat,
6 g fibre, 174 kcal (730 kJ)*

PUFFY SALMON PITA SANDWICHES

Use handy pantry ingredients to make this special lunch recipe when surprise guests drop in. Toasted whole wheat bread is a good replacement for pita breads.

1	can (7½ oz/213 g) salmon	1
¼ cup	light mayonnaise	50 mL
1	green onion, chopped	1
½ tsp	horseradish	2 mL
¼ tsp	dried thyme	1 mL
2	egg whites	2
Pinch	salt	Pinch
3	7-inch (18 cm) whole wheat pita bread rounds, split in half	3

• Remove skin from salmon and flake. In bowl, combine salmon, mayonnaise, green onion, horseradish and thyme. Beat egg whites and salt until stiff. Fold gently into salmon mixture.
• Place pitas on baking sheet. Spread each with salmon mixture, being careful to cover to edge of each pita. Bake in 400°F (200°C) oven for 12 to 15 minutes or until puffed and golden brown.

Makes 6 pita halves.
PREPARATION: 10 minutes
COOK: 12 to 15 minutes

Each serving: 2 pita halves

2 ☐ Starchy Choices
2½ ☑ Protein Choices
1 ▲ Fats & Oils Choice

*35 g carbohydrate, 19 g protein, 12 g fat,
5 g fibre, 330 kcal (1380 kJ)*

KITCHEN TIPS

• For chicken broth, use canned chicken broth, chicken bouillon cubes or homemade broth made by cooking bones and backs of cut-up chickens.
• Tomato paste is often needed in small amounts, so freeze remaining from this recipe in ice cube trays in 1 or 2 tbsp (15 or 25 mL) amounts.

MICROWAVE APPLESAUCE

Warm applesauce, one of life's greatest comfort foods! Using the microwave oven, cooking time is short and clean-up is minimal.

3½ cups	peeled, cored	875 mL
	and sliced cooking apples	
	(about 3 large Spy, Spartan or McIntosh)	
¾ cup	water	175 mL
¼ tsp	ground cinnamon	1 mL

• In 6-cup (1.5 L) microwavable dish, combine apple slices and water. Cover and microwave on High (100%) for 8 to 9 minutes or until apples are tender; stir once. Stir in cinnamon. Serve warm or at room temperature.

Makes 4 servings, 2 cups (500 mL).
PREPARATION: 10 minutes
COOK: 8 to 9 minutes

Each serving: ½ cup (125 mL)

1 ◪ Fruits & Vegetables Choice

*14 g carbohydrate, 0 g protein, 0 g fat,
2 g fibre, 53 kcal (220kJ)*

CREAMY RANCH SALAD DRESSING

A blender or food processor makes short work of this recipe. Use the dressing as both a salad dressing and a dip.

1 cup	low-fat cottage cheese	250 mL
⅔ cup	low-fat plain yogurt	150 mL
2	green onions, chopped	2
1 tsp	Dijon mustard	5 mL
½ tsp	garlic powder	2 mL
½ tsp	dried basil	2 mL
¼ tsp	dried oregano	1 mL

• In food processor or blender, process cottage cheese and yogurt until smooth. Pour into bowl and stir in onions and seasonings.
• Cover and refrigerate for at least 30 minutes so flavours develop. Store for up to one week. Stir before serving.

Makes 1⅔ cups (400 mL).
PREPARATION: 10 minutes
CHILL: 30 minutes or longer

Each serving: 3 tbsp (45 mL)

½ ◪ 2% Milk Choice

*3 g carbohydrate, 5 g protein, 1 g fat,
0 g fibre, 37 kcal (150 kJ)*

KITCHEN TIPS

• **Creamy Herb Dip:** For a dip, thin dressing with low-fat milk or water to desired consistency.
• **Tossed Green Salad:** Serve 3 tbsp (45 mL) dressing over approximately 2 cups (500 mL) salad greens.
• Salad dressing comparison: 3 tbsp (45 mL) commercial Ranch-style salad dressing = 216 calories; 3 tbsp (45 mL) Creamy Ranch Salad Dressing = 30 calories.

EGG DILL SANDWICH FILLING

Prepared the night before, this sandwich filling will make short work of lunch preparation in the morning.

4	hard-cooked eggs, chopped	4
1/4 cup	finely chopped cucumber	50 mL
2 tbsp	light mayonnaise	25 mL
1/4 tsp	dried dillweed	1 mL
1/4 tsp	salt	1 mL
Pinch	freshly ground pepper	Pinch

In bowl, combine chopped eggs, cucumber, mayonnaise and seasonings. Cover and refrigerate for up to one day.

Makes 4 servings, 1⅓ cups (325 mL).
PREPARATION: 20 minutes
CHILL: up to 1 day

Each serving: ⅓ cup (75 mL) filling

1 ▨ Protein Choice
1 ▲ Fats & Oils Choice
1 ▦ Extra

*2 g carbohydrate, 7 g protein, 7 g fat,
0 g fibre, 100 kcal (420 kJ)*

KITCHEN TIP

Raw cucumber provides moisture and flavour in this filling, resulting in less need for mayonnaise and therefore fewer calories from fat.

FAVOURITE CAESAR SALAD

Enjoy this lower-fat version of the famous Caesar salad. You'll have enough dressing for another meal.

Salad Dressing

3 tbsp	light mayonnaise	45 mL
1	clove garlic, minced	1
2 tbsp	red wine vinegar	25 mL
1 tbsp	Dijon mustard	15 mL
1 tbsp	lemon juice	15 mL
Dash	hot pepper sauce	Dash
Dash	Worcestershire sauce	Dash
1/4 cup	olive oil	50 mL
2 tbsp	water	25 mL

Salad

8 cups	torn romaine lettuce leaves (about 1 head)	2 L
1½ cups	toasted bread croutons	375 mL
1 tbsp	grated Parmesan cheese	15 mL

• Whisk together mayonnaise, garlic, vinegar, mustard, lemon juice, hot pepper sauce and Worcestershire sauce. Gradually whisk in olive oil and water until blended and smooth.
• Place torn lettuce, croutons and cheese in large salad bowl. Toss with ⅓ cup (75 mL) salad dressing (about one-half of dressing). Refrigerate remaining dressing for a second salad.

Makes 6 servings and ⅔ cup (150 mL) salad dressing.
PREPARATION: 15 minutes

Each serving: ⅙ of recipe

½ ◻ Starchy Choice
2 ▲ Fats & Oils Choices

*9 g carbohydrate, 2 g protein, 8 g fat,
1 g fibre, 119 kcal (500 kJ)*

KITCHEN TIP

For a single-serving of salad, use about 1 cup (250 mL) torn romaine lettuce leaves, 1/4 cup (50 mL) toasted bread croutons, 1 tbsp (15 mL) salad dressing and ½ tsp (2 mL) Parmesan cheese.

WEEKEND WARM RICE AND EGG SALAD

Since this luncheon recipe is a little more extensive in its preparation, we suggest you reserve it for weekends or holidays.

1½ cups	chicken broth	375 mL
⅔ cup	brown rice	150 mL
1 tsp	vegetable oil	5 mL
2	green onions, sliced	2
2 tsp	milk	10 mL
2	eggs	2
¼ tsp	salt	1 mL
Pinch	pepper	Pinch
1 tbsp	grated Parmesan cheese	15 mL
4 cups	torn salad greens*	1 L
1 tbsp	olive oil	15 mL
2 tsp	balsamic vinegar	10 mL
¼ cup	diced red pepper	50 mL

• In saucepan, cook chicken broth and rice, covered, on medium-low heat for about 40 minutes or until all liquid has been absorbed and rice is tender.
• In large nonstick skillet, heat vegetable oil on medium heat. Add onions and cook for 5 minutes.
• Whisk together milk, eggs, salt and pepper. Stir egg mixture into cooked rice. Stir egg-rice mixture into skillet. Heat for about 2 minutes; sprinkle with cheese.
• Place salad greens in large bowl. Combine olive oil and vinegar. Toss with greens and sprinkle with red pepper.
• Divide salad among three dinner plates; spoon rice mixture over each salad.

Makes 3 servings.
PREPARATION: 20 minutes
COOK: 40 minutes

Each serving: ⅓ of recipe. (1 cup/250 mL cooked rice mixture over ⅓ salad greens)

2 ☐ Starchy Choices
1 ☑ Protein Choice
2 ▲ Fats & Oils Choices

35 g carbohydrate, 12 g protein, 12 g fat, 3 g fibre, 298 kcal (1250 kJ)

OPEN-FACE COTTAGE CHEESE SANDWICHES

The open-face sandwich originated in Denmark. Take bread and the cottage cheese mixture in a tightly sealed container for lunch at your desk or prepare as a toasted sandwich for home.

1 cup	low-fat cottage cheese	250 mL
½ cup	chopped cucumber	125 mL
⅓ cup	shredded carrot (1 small)	75 mL
2 tbsp	chopped red or green pepper	25 mL
1 tbsp	light mayonnaise	15 mL
1 tsp	vinegar	5 mL
Pinch	freshly ground pepper	Pinch
6	slices whole wheat or rye bread	6

• In bowl, combine cottage cheese, cucumber, carrot, red or green pepper, mayonnaise, vinegar and pepper.
• Toast bread; top each slice with ⅓ cup (75 mL) filling. Cut into squares and serve.

Makes 6 open-face sandwiches.
PREPARATION: 10 minutes

Each serving: 1 open-face sandwich

1 ☐ Starchy Choice
1 ☑ Protein Choice

17 g carbohydrate, 8 g protein, 2 g fat, 2 g fibre, 114 kcal (480 kJ)

KITCHEN TIP

*Use a combination of lettuces, for instance Boston, iceberg and romaine.
  Wash and drain lettuce; tear into bite-sized pieces and dry in a towel or salad spinner. Lettuce will keep refrigerated for several days providing it is fairly dry. Place some paper towels or a clean tea towel in the plastic storage bag.

DINNER

Our menus provide the nutritious variety and appetizing meals the whole family enjoys. Of course, family members who do not need to restrict their energy intake may eat larger servings.

Measuring

Some of the prepared foods in the menus and recipes need to be measured so you know you have the right amount on your plate. We suggest you have a set of graduated "dry" measuring cups—the ones in $\frac{1}{4}$ cup, $\frac{1}{3}$ cup, $\frac{1}{2}$ cup and 1 cup (or 50 mL, 125 mL and 250 mL) sizes. These are also useful for measuring dry ingredients in recipes, so do double duty. Two or three pyrex, "liquid" measuring cups in 1 cup, 2 cup and possibly 4 cup sizes (or 250 mL, 500 mL and 1L) come in handy as well. Having measures at hand speeds up serving meals.

Accuracy in meat and cheese portions is particularly important because they have such a high calorie content. A scale is the most accurate and convenient means of measuring them. That's why the menus and recipes specify meat and cheese portions in grams, the metric weight used in most grocery stores.

Most of the time we give weights after cooking. However, when it makes more sense we provide the raw weight as purchased, for you to refer to when shopping.

Tips for Low-Fat Cooking

MEAT, FISH and POULTRY: Since most fat calories come from meat, we have specified lean cuts in our menus and recipes. It's easy to reduce the amount of fat found in many meat cuts. Simply trim off all visible fat and discard before cooking. Then by keeping serving sizes close to those suggested in the menus, you'll keep fat calories under control. Chicken, with the exception of roast chicken, should always be cooked without the skin to reduce fat and calories.

Fish used in the menus tends to be low in fat.

GRAVIES, SALAD DRESSINGS AND SAUCES: These usually high-fat foods are included in our menus but in lower-fat versions. See how to "trim the fat" in our Light Gravy recipe *(page 82)*.

Chill cooked soups containing meat. Fat that rises to the surface is easily removed along with a lot of calories.

Our sauces frequently use low-fat plain yogurt to replace higher-fat mayonnaise and sour cream without any loss of flavour. See Baked Potatoes with Creamy Cheese Sauce *(page 87)* and Yogurt Hollandaise Sauce *(page 85)*.

FLAVOURINGS: Squeezed juices and grated rinds of oranges, lemons and limes, and herbs and spices, all add marvellous flavour to foods. These "extras" highlight true food flavours.

PRODUCE: Nutritional guidelines *(page 9)* suggest we should all eat more vegetables. They help fill you up, have very little effect on your blood sugar and supply all the vitamins, minerals and fibre so important for health.

Our menus include vegetables and fruits you may not have tried before. They add variety to your table. Try them—you'll probably like them!

MEAL PLANNING: You probably are getting the message by now. If you are serious about weight loss and diabetes control, you will plan to have three balanced meals every day. This means a good breakfast, a moderate-sized lunch and not too large an evening meal (as well as whatever snacks you choose).

We have tried to include in our dinner menus many of your favourite comfort foods, updated to be lower in fat and calories. An occasional higher-fat dessert has been balanced against a low-fat main course.

DINNER RECIPES INDEX

HERB VINAIGRETTE DRESSING

Here's a zesty dressing to serve with leafy green salads or to drizzle over sliced cucumbers and tomatoes. And it doubles as a flavourful and tenderizing marinade for barbecuing meat. Truly versatile!

¼ cup	red wine vinegar	50 mL
¼ cup	chicken stock	50 mL
2 tbsp	lemon or lime juice	25 mL
1 tsp	dried tarragon, optional	5 mL
½ tsp	dry mustard	2 mL
½ tsp	paprika	2 mL
½ tsp	garlic salt	2 mL
¼ tsp	freshly ground pepper	1 mL
Dash	hot pepper sauce	Dash
2 tbsp	vegetable oil	25 mL

• In container with a tight-fitting lid, combine vinegar, chicken stock, lemon juice and seasonings; shake well. Add oil and shake again. Refrigerate for up to two weeks.

Makes ¾ cup (175 mL).
PREPARATION: *10 minutes*
CHILL: *up to 2 weeks*

Each serving: 2 tbsp (25 mL)

1 ▲ Fats & Oils Choice

1 g carbohydrate, 0 g protein, 5 g fat, 0 g fibre, 46 kcal (190 kJ)

KITCHEN TIPS

• **Marinade**: Use this dressing as a marinade for chicken, beef and pork as well as vegetables for barbecue kabobs *(Dinner Menu #3)*. Use about ⅓ cup (75 mL) dressing to marinate each 1 lb (500 g) of meat.
• Marinating meat in a sealed plastic bag improves flavour—and there's no washing up!
• If desired, you can replace chicken stock with beef stock when marinating beef.

LEMON BROCCOLI

A healthy choice! One serving of broccoli is an excellent source of vitamins A, C and folic acid as well as potassium and calcium and is also a source of dietary fibre.

1 lb	broccoli (about 3 stalks)	500 g
1 tsp	margarine or butter	5 mL
1	green onion, sliced	1
3 tbsp	chopped red pepper	45 mL
1 tbsp	lemon juice	15 mL
½ tsp	grated lemon rind	2 mL
Pinch	black pepper	Pinch

• Trim broccoli and cut lengthwise. Steam for about 8 minutes or until tender-crisp.
• In a skillet, melt margarine on medium-high heat. Add green onion and red pepper; sauté for 2 to 3 minutes. Add lemon juice, rind and pepper. Pour over cooked broccoli.

Makes 3 large servings.
PREPARATION: *10 minutes*
COOK: *10 minutes*

Each serving: ⅓ of recipe

½ ▱ Fruits & Vegetables Choice
½ ▲ Fats & Oils Choice

8 g carbohydrate, 4 g protein, 2 g fat, 3 g fibre, 52 kcal (220 kJ)

KITCHEN TIP

To choose fresh broccoli, look for a bunch with compact green heads and tight clusters. The buds are tiny and roll off into your hands. Steer clear of broccoli whose buds have turned yellow and bloomed— they are past their prime. The most tender stalks are the thin ones.

The best dressing is made with bread one or two days old. Stuff poultry just before you roast it. This recipe will stuff a 6-lb (3-kg) chicken; double the recipe for a 12-lb (6-kg) turkey.

6	slices bread (crusts included)	6
2 tbsp	margarine or butter	25 mL
1 cup	chopped mushrooms	250 mL
½ cup	chopped celery	125 mL
⅓ cup	chopped onion	75 mL
¼ cup	chopped parsley	50 mL
1 tsp	dried tarragon	5 mL
½ tsp	salt	2 mL
½ tsp	paprika	2 mL
Pinch	ground nutmeg and pepper	Pinch

• Prepare breadcrumbs in food processor or by hand.
• In nonstick skillet, melt margarine on medium-high heat. Add mushrooms, celery, onion, and parsley and cook for 5 minutes or until vegetables have softened. Cool. Stir in seasonings and add to breadcrumbs. (See below for poultry stuffing directions.)

Makes 6 servings, 4 cups (1 L).
PREPARATION: 20 minutes
COOK: 5 minutes for vegetables

Each serving: ⅔ cup (150 mL) dressing

1 ☐ Starchy Choice
1 ▲ Fats & Oils Choice

*16 g carbohydrate, 3 g protein, 5 g fat,
1 g fibre, 119 kcal (500 kJ)*

To stuff and roast poultry
Rinse and dry the cavity; stuff with prepared dressing. Close opening by trussing with a large needle and string or insert skewers and criss-cross the string. Cross legs over tail and tie with string so legs are close to the body. Turn wings back, tuck under the bird and secure with skewers or string.

Place on rack in open roasting pan, breast side up, with a meat thermometer inserted in thigh. Roast in 325°F (160°C) oven until thermometer reaches 185°F (85°C) or juices run clear. If breast starts to brown too much, cover loosely with foil.

To make perfect low-fat gravy for the roast chicken, prepare with pan drippings that have all visible fat removed.

	Pan juices	
	Water or vegetable liquid	
2 tbsp	cornstarch	25 mL
	Salt and pepper	

• Pour pan juices through a sieve into a 2-cup (500 mL) measuring cup. Skim fat with spoon or bulb baster; or drop ice cubes into the strained pan juices to chill fat layer, then remove hardened fat with ice.
• Add enough water or vegetable liquid to pan juices to measure 1½ cups (375 mL). Return to roasting pan; bring to boil.
• Mix cornstarch with 2 tbsp (25 mL) cold water. Gradually add to boiling liquid; cook and stir for about 5 minutes or until smooth and thickened. Season to taste with salt and pepper.

Makes 6 servings, 1½ cups (375 mL).
PREPARATION: 10 minutes
COOK: about 8 minutes

Variation

LIGHT BEEF GRAVY

• Prepare above recipe using roast beef pan juices.

Each serving: ¼ cup (50 mL)

1 ❖❖ Extra

*2 g carbohydrate, 1 g protein, 0 g fat,
0 g fibre, 14 kcal (60 kJ)*

KITCHEN TIP

If you have breadcrumbs in the freezer, approximately 3½ cups (875 mL) crumbs is the equivalent of 6 slices of bread.

We like this light, simply prepared and elegant ending to a meal. Truly attractive when served on a glass plate.

2	large pears, peeled, halved and cored	2
1/4 cup	dry red wine	50 mL
1/4 cup	water	50 mL
2	thin lemon slices, quartered	2
1 tsp	granulated sugar	5 mL
1/4 tsp	ground cinnamon	1 mL

• Place pears, cut side down, in shallow microwavable casserole. Combine wine, water, lemon pieces, sugar and cinnamon. Pour over pears, spooning some over each half.
• Cover and microwave on High (100%) for 6 to 8 minutes or until pears are tender. Cool, occasionally spooning juice over pears.

Makes 4 servings.
PREPARATION: 15 minutes
COOK: 6 to 8 minutes

**Each serving: 1 pear half and
2 tbsp (25 mL) juice**

1 ◩ Fruits & Vegetables Choice

*12 g carbohydrate, 0 g protein, 0 g fat,
2 g fibre, 51 kcal (210 kJ)*

When the weather outside is steamy, carefree, cool meals are important. Prepare this chilled salad ahead of time. It will come in very handy for last-minute meals.

2 1/3 cups	cubed peeled potatoes (3 medium)	575 mL
2	eggs	2
2/3 cup	sliced celery	150 mL
1/4 cup	sliced green onion	50 mL
1/4 cup	chopped parsley	50 mL
1/4 cup	light mayonnaise	50 mL
1/4 cup	low-fat plain yogurt	50 mL
1 tbsp	malt vinegar	15 mL
1/2 tsp	each salt and dried tarragon	2 mL
1/4 tsp	dry mustard	1 mL
1/4 tsp	freshly ground pepper	1 mL
	Leaf lettuce	

• In saucepan, cook potatoes in boiling water for about 10 minutes or until just tender; drain and cool. Simmer eggs in water in separate saucepan for about 20 minutes. Drain well and cool. Peel and cut eggs into quarters; set aside.
• Combine potatoes, celery, onion and parsley.
• Stir together mayonnaise, yogurt, vinegar and seasonings. Stir gently into potato mixture. Place in a bowl lined with lettuce leaves and garnish with egg quarters. Cover and chill until serving time.

Makes 7 servings, 3½ cups (875 mL) salad.
PREPARATION: 30 minutes
CHILL: 30 minutes or longer

Each serving: ½ cup (125 mL)

1 ◻ Starchy Choice
1 ◢ Fats & Oils Choice

*16 g carbohydrate, 4 g protein, 4 g fat,
1 g fibre, 115 kcal (480 kJ)*

BAKED VEGETABLE MEAT LOAF

Vegetables add extra flavour and moisture to this favourite recipe.

1 lb	lean ground beef	500 g
½ cup	rolled oats	125 mL
⅓ cup	finely chopped carrot	75 mL
⅓ cup	finely chopped celery	75 mL
3 tbsp	finely chopped onion	45 mL
3 tbsp	chopped parsley	45 mL
½ cup	tomato sauce	125 mL
1	egg, lightly beaten	1
2 tsp	prepared mustard	10 mL
¼ tsp	salt	1 mL
¼ tsp	freshly ground pepper	1 mL
¼ tsp	chili powder	1 mL

• Spray 5x9-inch (2 L) loaf pan with nonstick coating.
• In large bowl, combine beef, rolled oats, carrot, celery, onion and parsley; mix well.
• Combine tomato sauce, egg and seasonings. Lightly combine meat mixture with tomato mixture just until mixed. Turn into loaf pan.
• Bake in 375°F (190°C) oven for 50 to 60 minutes. Drain off any fat. Allow to stand for 5 minutes before slicing into six slices.

Makes 6 servings.
PREPARATION: *20 minutes*
COOK: *50 to 60 minutes*

Each serving: ⅙ of recipe
½ ☐ Starchy Choice 2½ ☑ Protein Choices
8 g carbohydrate, 17 g protein, 10 g fat, 2 g fibre, 187 kcal (780 kJ)

INDIVIDUAL MICROWAVE MUESLI FRUIT CRISPS

Oatmeal fruit crisps are one of those true comfort desserts enjoyed at all times of year.

Apple Crisp

½	medium apple, peeled and sliced (about ½ cup/125 mL)	½
2 tbsp	water	25 mL
2 tbsp	**Rolled Oat Muesli** (*page 59*)	25 mL
1 tsp	lightly packed brown sugar	5 mL
1 tsp	granulated brown low-calorie sweetener	5 mL
Pinch	ground cinnamon	Pinch

• Place apple slices and water in small custard cup. Combine Rolled Oat Muesli, brown sugar, sweetener and cinnamon. Sprinkle over apple. Microwave*, uncovered, at High (100%) for 2 to 2½ minutes or until apples are tender.
*To bake in the oven, allow 20 minutes at 350°F (180°C).

Makes 1 serving.
PREPARATION: *5 minutes if Muesli Rolled Oats is prepared*
COOK: *about 2 minutes per flavour*

Variations

APPLESAUCE CRISP

• Replace ½ medium apple and 2 tbsp (25 mL) water with ⅓ cup (75 mL) unsweetened applesauce. Add pinch nutmeg. Microwave, uncovered, at High (100%) for 1 to 1½ minutes.

BLUEBERRY CRISP

• Replace ½ medium apple with ½ cup (125 mL) fresh or frozen blueberries, lightly packed brown sugar with granulated sugar, granulated brown low-calorie sweetener with granulated white low-calorie sweetener, cinnamon with ginger. Microwave, uncovered, at High (100%) for 2 to 2½ minutes or until blueberries are cooked.

Each serving: 1 crisp
½ ☐ Starchy Choice 1 ☑ Fruits & Vegetables Choice ½ ▲ Fats & Oils Choice
20 g carbohydrate, 2 g protein, 2 g fat, 3 g fibre, 99 kcal (420 kJ)

YOGURT HOLLANDAISE SAUCE

Replace rich, high-calorie sauces with this tangy, quickly prepared version of the classic sauce.

¾ cup	low-fat plain yogurt	175 mL
1	egg, lightly beaten	1
1 tsp	cornstarch	5 mL
¼ tsp	prepared mustard	1 mL
¼ tsp	salt	1 mL
Dash	hot pepper sauce	Dash
Pinch	paprika	Pinch

• In saucepan, whisk together yogurt, egg, cornstarch, mustard and seasonings. Cook over medium heat, stirring constantly, for about 5 minutes or until thickened.

Makes 4 servings, 1 cup (250 mL).
PREPARATION: 5 minutes
COOK: 5 minutes

Variations

Use these sauce variations over cooked vegetables or for poached eggs on toasted English muffin halves.

LEMON HOLLANDAISE

• Add 1 tsp (5 mL) lemon juice and ½ tsp (2 mL) grated lemon rind. Cook as above.

HERBED HOLLANDAISE

• Add ¼ tsp (1 mL) each dried tarragon and thyme. Cook as above.

PARMESAN HOLLANDAISE

• Add 1 tbsp (15 mL) grated Parmesan cheese. Cook as above.

Each serving: ¼ cup (50 mL)
1 ◆ 2% Milk Choice
4 g carbohydrate, 4 g protein, 2 g fat, 0 g fibre, 51 kcal (210 kJ)

BAKED FISH EN PAPILLOTE

"En papillote" means steaming in parchment paper or aluminum foil. It is a fast and healthy way to bake a complete meal in a package. Choose fish that can be cut into fairly thick pieces, for example turbot, halibut or haddock.

1	pkg (400 g) frozen and thawed fish	1
½ cup	finely chopped carrot (1 medium)	125 mL
4	large mushrooms, sliced	4
1	green onion, chopped	1
¼ cup	chopped parsley	50 mL
1 tbsp	lemon juice	15 mL
1 tbsp	melted margarine or butter	15 mL
½ tsp	dried thyme	2 mL
	Salt and pepper to taste	

• Cut four sheets of parchment paper or aluminum foil into squares 2 inches (5 cm) larger than fish fillets. Spray paper or foil with nonstick coating. Cut fish into four equal-size pieces; place in centre of paper or foil.
• Distribute carrot, mushrooms and onion evenly over fish.
• Combine parsley, lemon juice, margarine and seasonings. Spoon over vegetables. Fold long ends of paper or foil twice so fish is tightly enclosed. Lift short ends, bring together and fold twice. Place on baking pan.
• Bake in 400°F (200°C) oven 20 to 25 minutes or until fish flakes easily with a fork and vegetables are tender. Place packages on dinner plates for each person to open at the table.

Makes 4 servings.
PREPARATION: 15 minutes
COOK: 20 to 25 minutes

Each serving: ¼ of recipe
3 ◪ Protein Choices 1 ▦ Extra
3 g carbohydrate, 20 g protein, 4 g fat, 1 g fibre, 131 kcal (550 kJ)

VEGETABLE SPAGHETTI SAUCE

You'll be amazed at how many uses you will find for this inexpensive vegetarian sauce. Use it for lasagna, as a sauce over chicken or with ground beef as a more traditional sauce for spaghetti. So ... make lots and freeze.

1 tbsp	vegetable oil	15 mL
3 cups	finely chopped zucchini (3 medium)	750 mL
1 cup	chopped onion (1 medium)	250 mL
½ cup	finely chopped carrot (1 medium)	125 mL
2	cloves garlic, minced	2
1	can (28 oz/796 mL) tomatoes	1
1	can (7.5 oz/213 mL) tomato sauce	1
1	can (10 oz/284 mL) mushroom stems and pieces	1
2 tsp	dried oregano	10 mL
1½ tsp	dried basil	7 mL
1 tsp	salt	5 mL
¼ tsp	pepper	1 mL

• In large saucepan, heat oil over medium-high heat. Add zucchini, onion, carrot and garlic. Cook for 10 minutes or until onions are tender; stir frequently. Break up tomatoes. Add tomatoes and liquid, tomato sauce, mushrooms and liquid and seasonings. Cover and simmer for 2 hours or until sauce is thickened; stir occasionally.

Makes 6 servings, 6 cups (1.5 L) sauce.
PREPARATION: 20 minutes
COOK: 2 hours

Each serving: 1 cup (250 mL)

1 ◨ Fruits & Vegetables Choice
1 ▲ Fats & Oils Choice

*15 g carbohydrate, 3 g protein, 3 g fat,
4 g fibre, 88 kcal (370 kJ)*

Variation

BEEF AND VEGETABLE SPAGHETTI SAUCE

• Cook ½ lb (250 g) lean ground beef until brown and crumbly; drain fat. Add to ingredients for Vegetable Spaghetti Sauce and cook as recipe directs.

Makes 8 servings, about 8 cups (2 L) sauce.

Each serving: 1 cup (250 mL)

1 ◨ Fruits & Vegetables Choice
1½ ◨ Protein Choices
½ ▲ Fats & Oils Choice

*15 g carbohydrate, 10 g protein, 6 g fat,
4 g fibre, 148 kcal (620 kJ)*

KITCHEN TIP

Double the recipe and freeze Vegetable Spaghetti Sauce for future meals:
• 4 cups (1L) for Vegetarian Lasagna *(page 93)*
• 2 cups (500 mL) for Chicken Cacciatore *(page 98)*
• 6 cups (1.5L) for Beef and Vegetable Spaghetti Sauce *(see above)*

BAKED POTATOES WITH CREAMY CHEESE SAUCE

Dress up baked potatoes with this tangy sauce instead of sour cream.

2	medium baking potatoes	2
	(5-inch/12 cm long)	

Sauce		
½ cup	buttermilk	125 mL
2 tbsp	grated Parmesan cheese	25 mL
1 tsp	cornstarch	5 mL
½ tsp	Dijon mustard	2 mL
Pinch	salt and freshly ground pepper	Pinch

Potatoes
• Scrub potatoes and prick with a fork. Bake in 375°F (190°C) oven for 1 hour or until tender, or microwave on High (100%) for 6 to 7 minutes or until tender.

Sauce: Stove-top
• In small saucepan, combine buttermilk, cheese, cornstarch, mustard, salt and pepper. Bring to a boil, reduce heat to low, and simmer, stirring constantly, for 3 minutes or until thickened.

Sauce: Microwave
• Stir together buttermilk, cheese, cornstarch, mustard and seasonings in 1 cup (250 mL) glass measure. Microwave on Medium-High (70%) for 1½ to 2 minutes; stir twice. Cook for another 30 seconds or until smooth and thickened.

• Cut potatoes in half; fluff pulp in each half with a fork. Pour 2 tbsp (25 mL) sauce on each half.

Makes 4 servings, 4 potato halves and ½ cup (125 mL) sauce.
PREPARATION: 15 minutes
COOK: 1 hour

Each serving: ½ potato and 2 tbsp (25 mL) sauce

1 ☐ Starchy Choice

17 g carbohydrate, 3 g protein, 1 g fat, 1 g fibre, 89 kcal (370 kJ)

STRAWBERRY AND BANANA RICE PUDDING

Combine these two favourite fruits with creamy cooked rice for a "comfort" dessert. An ideal use for leftover cooked rice.

½ cup	uncooked rice **or**	125 mL
1⅓ cups	cooked rice	325 mL
1 cup	water	250 mL
1½ cups	skim milk	375 mL
1 tsp	vanilla extract	5 mL
1 tbsp	brown sugar	15 mL
1	ripe medium banana, mashed	1
1 cup	sliced strawberries	250 mL
	(about 6 large)	
½ cup	light sour cream	125 mL
	Ground cinnamon	

• In heavy saucepan, cook rice and water, covered, on medium-low heat for about 15 minutes or until all water is absorbed and rice is tender. (Omit this step if leftover cooked rice is being used.)
• Add milk to cooked rice in saucepan. Cook, uncovered, over medium-low heat for about 15 minutes or until thick and creamy; stir frequently to prevent rice and milk from scorching. Remove from heat; stir in vanilla and brown sugar. Cool.
• Before serving, fold in mashed banana, strawberries and sour cream. Sprinkle each serving with cinnamon.

Makes 8 servings, 4 cups (1 L).
PREPARATION: 10 minutes
COOK: 30 minutes

Each serving: ½ cup (125 mL)

½ ☐ Starchy Choice
1 ◪ Fruits & Vegetables Choice
½ ◆ 2% Milk Choice

20 g carbohydrate, 4 g protein, 2 g fat, 1 g fibre, 111 kcal (460 kJ)

KITCHEN TIP

For best results when cooking rice, use double the amount of water to rice and cook tightly covered. No peeking allowed.

ORIENTAL CHICKEN STIR-FRY

Stir-fry recipes provide a delicious way of adding lots of vegetables to a small amount of meat.

1 tbsp	vegetable oil	15 mL
¾ lb	boneless chicken breast, cut into thin strips	375 g
2 cups	broccoli florets	500 mL
⅔ cup	chopped red pepper	150 mL
3	green onions, diagonally sliced	3
1	clove garlic, minced	1
2 cups	sliced mushrooms	500 mL
1 cup	sliced celery	250 mL
½ cup	chicken broth	125 mL
1 tbsp	cornstarch	15 mL
2 tsp	soy sauce	10 mL
½ tsp	ground ginger	2 mL

• In wok or large heavy nonstick skillet, heat oil over high heat. Add chicken; cook for 3 minutes stirring constantly.
• Add broccoli, red pepper, onions and garlic; cover and steam for 5 minutes.
• Add mushrooms and celery; cover and steam for 2 minutes.
• Combine chicken broth, cornstarch, soy sauce and ginger; pour over chicken mixture. Stir-fry for 1 minute, or until sauce thickens.

Makes 4 servings.
PREPARATION: 20 minutes
COOK: 11 minutes for stir-fry

Each serving: ¼ of recipe

½ ◪ Fruits & Vegetables Choice
3 ◪ Protein Choices
1 ▪▪ Extra

8 g carbohydrate, 22 g protein, 6 g fat, 2 g fibre, 174 kcal (730 kJ)

FRENCH-STYLE PEAS WITH LETTUCE

The lettuce supplies moisture to allow the peas to steam gently. Frozen taste like fresh!

2 tsp	margarine or butter	10 mL
1 cup	thinly sliced iceberg lettuce	250 mL
2 cups	frozen peas	500 mL
2	chopped green onions	2
1 tsp	chicken bouillon powder	5 mL
¼ tsp	salt	1 mL
¼ tsp	dried marjoram	1 mL

• In saucepan, melt margarine; place lettuce in pan, top with frozen peas and onions. Sprinkle with bouillon and seasonings.
• Cook, covered, over medium heat for 4 to 6 minutes or until peas are just cooked; stir occasionally. Serve immediately.

Makes 5 servings.
PREPARATION: 10 minutes
COOK: 4 to 6 minutes

Each serving: ½ cup (125 mL)

½ ◪ Fruits & Vegetables Choice
½ ▲ Fats & Oils Choice

8 g carbohydrate, 3 g protein, 2 g fat, 3 g fibre, 59 kcal (250 kJ)

KITCHEN TIPS

• Prepare chicken broth with 1 chicken bouillon cube or 1 sachet chicken bouillon powder dissolved in ½ cup (125 mL) water. Look for brands with less salt.
• To make a stir-fry dinner easy, have all the ingredients cut and ready to use.
• Remember, a little fat goes a long way in stir-fry cooking. Use a nonstick skillet or wok to further reduce the amount of fat needed.

PROVENÇALE PORK CHOP AND RICE DINNER

Ultimate convenience in meal preparation translates into a recipe for a "meal in a dish." Popular pork or chicken in combination with rice and vegetables makes this a very easily prepared meal.

5	lean pork chops cut ½-inch (1 cm) thick	5
½ tsp	salt	2 mL
¼ tsp	pepper	1 mL

Vegetable-Rice

½ cup	chopped onion (1 small)	125 mL
½ cup	chopped green pepper	125 mL
¼ cup	water	50 mL
1	can (28 oz/796 mL) tomatoes	1
¾ cup	long grain white rice	175 mL
1 tsp	garlic powder	5 mL

• Trim and discard excess fat from chops. Sprinkle chops with salt and pepper. In large nonstick skillet, brown chops over medium heat on both sides. Remove to deep 6-cup (1.5 L) casserole.

• In same skillet, cook onion and green pepper in water for about 5 minutes. Chop tomatoes; combine undrained tomatoes with vegetables, rice and garlic powder. Spoon over meat in casserole.

• Cover and bake in 325°F (160°C) oven for about 1¼ hours or until liquid is absorbed and rice is cooked.

Makes 5 servings, 5 chops and 5 cups (1.25 L) rice.
PREPARATION: 20 minutes
COOK: 1¼ hours

Each serving: 1 chop and 1 cup (250 mL) vegetable-rice

1½ ☐ Starchy Choices
½ ◨ Fruits & Vegetables Choice
3½ ◪ Protein Choices

31 g carbohydrate, 29 g protein, 10 g fat, 2 g fibre, 335 kcal (1400 kJ)

Variation

PROVENÇALE CHICKEN AND RICE DINNER

• Remove and discard skin and fat from 5 large chicken thighs or drumsticks (1½ lb/750 g); prepare according to recipe.

Each serving: 1 chicken thigh and 1 cup (250 mL) vegetable-rice

1½ ☐ Starchy Choices
½ ◨ Fruits & Vegetables Choice
3 ◪ Protein Choices

31 g carbohydrate, 24 g protein, 7 g fat, 2 g fibre, 283 kcal (1180 kJ)

All the taste of regular french fries, with less than half the calories! This oven-baked method is a fast and lower-fat method of cooking fried potatoes. Cut potatoes in either round slices or long, thin french-fry sticks.

6	medium* unpeeled potatoes	6
3 tbsp	melted margarine or butter	45 mL
1 to 2 tsp	garlic powder	5 to 10 mL
¾ tsp	salt	4 mL
¼ tsp	pepper	1 mL

• In saucepan, parboil potatoes in boiling water for 10 minutes; drain well and cool until easy to handle. Cut into ½-inch (1 cm) round slices or french-fry sticks.
• Place potatoes on baking pan. Combine margarine and seasonings; spoon over potatoes.
• Bake in 375°F (190°C) oven for 12 to 15 minutes; turn potatoes and bake for 12 to 15 minutes longer or until tender and browned.

Makes 6 servings.
PREPARATION: 10 minutes
COOK: about 24 minutes

Each serving: ⅙ of recipe

2 ☐ Starchy Choices
1 ▲ Fats & Oils Choice

28 g carbohydrate, 3 g protein, 6 g fat, 2 g fibre, 172 kcal (720 kJ)

KITCHEN TIP

*A **medium** potato is about 5 inches (12 cm) long and 2½ inches (6 cm) in diameter.

When garden-fresh tomatoes are at their best price, stuff them with extra vegetables. They add lots of colour and flavour to your dinner plate.

4	medium tomatoes	4
½ cup	chopped fresh mushrooms	125 mL
½ cup	chopped onion (1 small)	125 mL
⅓ cup	kernel corn	75 mL
1 tsp	margarine or butter	5 mL
1 tbsp	grated Parmesan cheese	15 mL
1 tbsp	minced parsley	15 mL
1 tbsp	dried breadcrumbs	15 mL
¼ tsp	salt	1 mL
Pinch	each: pepper and cayenne	Pinch

• Cut thin slice from stem end of each tomato. Scoop out seeds and some pulp; reserve pulp. Turn tomatoes upside down on rack to drain while preparing filling.
• Cook tomato pulp, mushrooms, onion and corn in margarine over medium-high heat for 5 minutes or until partially cooked and liquid is reduced. Stir in cheese, parsley, breadcrumbs and seasonings.
• Spoon corn mixture into tomatoes. Bake in shallow pan in 350°F (180°C) oven for about 20 minutes or until tomatoes are tender.

Makes 4 servings.
PREPARATION: 15 minutes
COOK: 15 to 20 minutes

Each serving: 1 tomato

1 ◪ Fruits & Vegetables Choice
½ ▲ Fats & Oils Choice

11 g carbohydrate, 3 g protein, 2 g fat, 2 g fibre, 64 kcal (270 kJ)

CURRIED RICE

We enjoy the flavours in this rice dish, which are similar to but milder than those used in traditional curries.

1 tbsp	vegetable oil, divided	15 mL
1 tsp	minced gingerroot **or**	5 mL
1/4 tsp	ground ginger	1 mL
1	medium clove garlic, minced	1
1 tbsp	curry powder	15 mL
4	green onions, chopped	4
1 cup	long grain white rice	250 mL
2 cups	beef broth*	500 mL
1/2	medium green pepper, diced	1/2
1/2	medium red pepper, diced	1/2
1/4 cup	chopped parsley	50 mL

• In saucepan, heat 1 tsp (5 mL) oil over medium heat; add gingerroot and garlic. Cook, stirring constantly, for about 2 minutes or until garlic is golden. Stir in curry powder, then remove and reserve curry mixture.
• Add 2 tsp (10 mL) oil and green onions to same saucepan. Cook on high heat for 1 minute. Add rice and beef broth. Cover and cook on medium-low for 20 minutes or until all liquid has been absorbed and rice is tender. Stir in reserved curry mixture, green and red pepper and parsley. Allow to stand for 5 minutes before serving.

Makes 6 servings, 4 cups (1 L).
PREPARATION: 20 minutes
COOK: 20 minutes

Each serving: 2/3 cup (150 mL)

2 ▢ Starchy Choices
1/2 ▲ Fats & Oils Choice

29 g carbohydrate, 4 g protein, 3 g fat, 1 g fibre, 156 kcal (650 kJ)

KITCHEN TIP

*To make 2 cups (500 mL) beef broth, use 2 cups (500 mL) water and 2 beef bouillon cubes or 2 sachets beef bouillon powder or approximately 2 tsp (10 mL) liquid beef bouillon concentrate. Some have less salt.

CRISPY BAKED CHICKEN

Take advantage of supermarket specials on chicken for this dish. Seasoned dried breadcrumbs provide a pleasantly crusty coating.

6	small chicken thighs or drumsticks (about 1 1/4 lb/625 g)	6
1/2 cup	low-fat plain yogurt	125 mL
1 tbsp	Dijon mustard	15 mL
1 tsp	minced gingerroot	5 mL
1/2 cup	fine dried breadcrumbs	125 mL
1 tsp	garlic salt	5 mL
1/4 tsp	pepper	1 mL
1/4 tsp	curry powder	1 mL
1/4 tsp	paprika	1 mL

• Remove and discard skin and fat from chicken pieces.
• In shallow dish, combine yogurt, mustard and gingerroot; set aside. In second dish, stir together breadcrumbs and seasonings.
• Dip chicken first into yogurt, then into breadcrumbs. Place on baking pan sprayed with nonstick coating.
• Bake in 350°F (180°C) oven for about 40 minutes or until cooked through and golden brown.

Makes 3 servings.
PREPARATION: 15 minutes
COOK: 40 minutes

Each serving: 1/3 of recipe (2 pieces chicken)

1 ▢ Starchy Choice
4 ▨ Protein Choices

16 g carbohydrate, 31 g protein, 10 g fat, 0 g fibre, 285 kcal (1190 kJ)

MINTED CARROTS AND SNOW PEAS

A different way to serve peas and carrots—and rich in vitamins A and C.

1½ cups	sliced carrot (3 medium)	375 mL
2 cups	trimmed snow peas	500 mL
1 tbsp	margarine or butter	15 mL
1 tbsp	lemon juice	15 mL
1 tbsp	chopped fresh mint **or**	15 mL
1 tsp	dried mint	5 mL

• Cook carrot in a small amount of boiling water for about 10 minutes or until tender. Add peas during last 5 minutes of cooking (do not overcook). Drain well. Stir in margarine, lemon juice and mint.

Makes 3 servings.
PREPARATION: 10 minutes
COOK: 10 minutes

Each serving: ⅔ cup (150 mL)

½ ◪ Fruits & Vegetables Choice
1 ▲ Fats & Oils Choice
1 ▨ Extra

*10 g carbohydrate, 3 g protein, 4 g fat,
4 g fibre, 81 kcal (340 kJ)*

SEAFOOD PASTA SAUCE

Most of us have a lingering love affair with pasta. Serve this low-fat seafood and vegetable sauce over your choice of pasta.

2½ cups	thinly sliced zucchini (2 small)	625 mL
1½ cups	thinly sliced carrot (3 medium)	375 mL
1½ cups	low-fat plain yogurt	375 mL
1 tbsp	all purpose flour	15 mL
¼ tsp	ground nutmeg	1 mL
Pinch	each: salt and cayenne pepper	Pinch
⅓ cup	grated Parmesan cheese	75 mL
1	can (7 oz/198 g) water-packed tuna, drained and flaked	1
1	can (4 oz/113 g) shrimp, rinsed and drained	1

• In medium saucepan, cook zucchini and carrot in small amount of boiling water for 3 to 4 minutes; drain and reserve.
• In saucepan, combine yogurt, flour and seasonings. Cook, slowly, over low heat, until hot. Add cheese, tuna, shrimp, carrots and zucchini; heat slowly.

Makes 4 servings, 5 cups (1.25 L).
PREPARATION: 15 minutes
COOK: about 10 minutes

**Each serving: 1¼ cups (300 mL) sauce
(without pasta)**

½ ◪ Fruits & Vegetables Choice
1 ◪ 2% Milk Choice
2½ ◪ Protein Choices
1 ▨ Extra

*15 g carbohydrate, 24 g protein, 4 g fat,
2 g fibre, 194 kcal (810 kJ)*

KITCHEN TIP

Leftover sauce may be frozen in 1¼-cup (300 mL) servings.

VEGETARIAN LASAGNA

A great use for frozen Vegetable Spaghetti Sauce. This vegetarian version of lasagna not only provides an ample serving but also is very high in fibre.

8	lasagna noodles	8
2	pkgs (300 g) frozen chopped spinach, thawed and well drained	2
1	carton (500 g) low-fat cottage cheese	1
1	egg	1
½ tsp	salt	2 mL
¼ tsp	pepper	1 mL
¼ tsp	ground nutmeg	1 mL
4 cups	**Vegetable Spaghetti Sauce** (page 86)	1 L
1½ cups	shredded part-skim mozzarella cheese	375 mL
2 tbsp	grated Parmesan cheese	25 mL

• In large pot of boiling water, cook lasagna according to package directions or until al dente (tender but firm). Drain well and set aside.
• Combine spinach, cottage cheese, egg and seasonings.
• Spread 1 cup (250 mL) spaghetti sauce in 13x9-inch (3.5 L) baking pan. Place 4 noodles, overlapping, over sauce; add one-half spinach mixture and one-half remaining spaghetti sauce; repeat layers. Sprinkle evenly with mozzarella and Parmesan cheeses.
• Bake in 350°F (180°C) oven for about 1 hour or until hot and bubbly; let stand 10 minutes before cutting into six servings.

Makes 6 servings.
PREPARATION: 20 minutes if Vegetable Spaghetti Sauce is prepared
COOK: 60 minutes

Each serving: ⅙ of recipe

1½ ☐ Starchy Choices
1 ◪ Fruits & Vegetables Choice
3 ◪ Protein Choices

36 g carbohydrate, 26 g protein, 9 g fat, 6 g fibre, 325 kcal (1360 kJ)

OVEN BEEF STEW

This savoury beef stew will be welcome on a cold blustery day. Cooking for one? Individual portions freeze well.

¼ cup	all purpose flour	50 mL
½ tsp	salt	2 mL
½ tsp	each: paprika and dried thyme	2 mL
¼ tsp	pepper	1 mL
1¼ lb	lean stewing beef	625 g
1 tbsp	vegetable oil	15 mL
1¼ cups	water	300 mL
1	pkg (36 g) onion soup mix	1
1	bay leaf	1
4	small potatoes, cut into wedges	4
3	small onions, cut into wedges	3
1	medium carrot, sliced	1
2 cups	sliced mushrooms	500 mL

• Combine flour and seasonings in plastic bag. Trim and discard all visible fat from beef. Cut beef into 1-inch (2.5 cm) cubes. Lightly toss beef in seasoned flour; reserve excess flour.
• Add oil to 6 cup (1.5 L) oven-proof casserole; stir in floured meat. Bake, uncovered, in 450°F (230°C) oven for 30 minutes; stir once.
• Reduce oven temperature to 350°F (180°C). Combine water, onion soup mix, reserved flour and bay leaf. Pour over meat.
• Bake, covered, for 1 hour; stir once. Add potatoes, onions, carrot and mushrooms and ¼ cup (50 mL) water, if needed. Bake, covered, for about 45 minutes or until meat and vegetables are tender. Discard bay leaf.

Makes 6 servings.
PREPARATION: 20 minutes
COOK: 2¼ hours

Each serving: 1⅓ cups (325 mL)

1 ☐ Starchy Choice
1 ◪ Fruits & Vegetables Choice
3 ◪ Protein Choices

26 g carbohydrate, 25 g protein, 9 g fat, 3 g fibre, 284 kcal (1190 kJ)

NEWFOUNDLAND FISH CASSEROLE

This recipe was given to us by a friend from the Maritimes. On hectic days, prepare this tangy casserole in the morning, refrigerate, then bake for dinner.

1½	slices whole wheat bread	1½
1	pkg (400 g) fish fillets, thawed (cod, turbot, haddock, halibut)	1
2 tbsp	chopped onion	25 mL
2 tbsp	margarine or butter, melted	25 mL
1 tbsp	lemon juice	15 mL
1 tbsp	Worcestershire sauce	15 mL
1 tbsp	vinegar	15 mL
1 tsp	Dijon mustard	5 mL
Pinch	each: savory, paprika, salt and pepper	Pinch

• Spray 4-cup (1 L) casserole with nonstick coating.
• Prepare coarse breadcrumbs in food processor or by hand. Place half of crumbs in casserole.
• Cut fish into 4 large chunks; place over breadcrumbs. Sprinkle with chopped onion and top with remaining crumbs.
• Combine melted margarine, lemon juice, Worcestershire sauce, vinegar, mustard and seasonings. Pour over crumbs.
• Cover and bake in 400°F (200°C) oven for 25 to 30 minutes. Uncover and bake for 15 minutes longer or until surface is brown and fish flakes easily with a fork.

Makes 4 servings.
PREPARATION: 15 minutes
COOK: 40 to 45 minutes

Each serving: ¼ of recipe

½ ☐ Starchy Choice
2½ ☑ Protein Choices

7 g carbohydrate, 19 g protein, 7 g fat, 1 g fibre, 165 kcal (690 kJ)

CHILI CON CARNE

Chili tucked away in the freezer is always helpful on busy days. This recipe makes a large amount thanks to the addition of "extra" vegetables.

1 lb	lean ground beef	500 g
1 cup	chopped onion (1 medium)	250 mL
1	clove garlic, crushed	1
3 cups	finely shredded cabbage	750 mL
2 cups	thinly sliced celery	500 mL
½ cup	chopped green pepper (½ medium)	125 mL
1	can (28 oz/796 mL) tomatoes	1
1	can (7.5 oz/213 mL) tomato sauce	1
1	can (19 oz/540 mL) kidney beans, drained	1
1 tbsp	chili powder	15 mL
1 tsp	dried oregano	5 mL
1 tsp	salt	5 mL
¼ tsp	hot pepper sauce	1 mL

• In large nonstick skillet, cook beef over medium-high heat until brown and crumbly. Drain off fat. Add onion and garlic; cook for 5 minutes.
• Add cabbage, celery, green pepper, tomatoes with juice, tomato sauce, kidney beans and seasonings. Cover and simmer over medium-low heat for 45 minutes or until vegetables are tender; stir occasionally.

Makes about 8 servings, 9 cups (2.25 L).
PREPARATION: 20 minutes
COOK: about 45 minutes

Each serving: 1¼ cups (300 mL)

1 ☐ Starchy Choice
2 ☑ Protein Choices

21 g carbohydrate, 16 g protein, 6 g fat, 7 g fibre, 195 kcal (820 kJ)

KITCHEN TIP

To freeze extra chili, portion into single-size plastic containers. Good use for all those yogurt or margarine containers everyone saves.

Enjoy this easily prepared spicy relish in sandwiches or with roast chicken, ham or turkey.

1½ cups	cranberries	375 mL
1	small unpeeled orange, seeded and coarsely chopped	1
1	medium unpeeled apple, cored and coarsely chopped	1
⅓ cup	water	75 mL
¼ cup	granulated sugar	50 mL
¼ tsp	ground ginger	1 mL
¼ tsp	ground nutmeg	1 mL

• In food processor or blender container, process cranberries, orange and apple until finely chopped. Place in shallow microwavable casserole. Stir in water, sugar, ginger and nutmeg.
• Microwave on High (100%) for 3 to 4 minutes; stir. Microwave on Medium (50%) for 2 to 3 minutes; cool slightly. Cover and refrigerate for up to two weeks.

Makes 9 servings, 2¼ cups (550 mL) sauce.
PREPARATION: *10 minutes*
CHILL: *up to 2 weeks*

Each serving: ¼ cup (50 mL)

1 ▨ Fruits & Vegetables Choice

12 g carbohydrate, 0 g protein, 0 g fat, 2 g fibre, 45 kcal (190 kJ)

or

Each serving: 1 level tbsp (15 mL)

1 ▨ Extra

3 g carbohydrate, 0 g protein, 0 g fat, 1 g fibre, 11 kcal (50 kJ)

KITCHEN TIP

Freeze bags of cranberries in the fall when they are in season. Then you will be able to make this relish throughout the year.

SCALLOPED POTATOES

A favourite of ours, this recipe has about one-half the fat of traditional scalloped potatoes.

3½ cups	cubed potatoes (4 medium)	875 mL
1	medium onion, thinly sliced	1
½ tsp	salt, divided	2 mL
¼ tsp	pepper, divided	1 mL
2 tbsp	margarine or butter	25 mL
½ cup	skim milk	125 mL
2 tbsp	grated Parmesan cheese	25 mL

• Lightly spray an 8-inch (20 cm) baking pan or casserole with nonstick coating. Layer one-half the potato slices in pan; top with one-half the onions and sprinkle with one-half the salt and pepper. Repeat layers.
• Heat milk and margarine to boiling; pour over potatoes. Sprinkle with cheese.
• Cover and bake in 350°F (180°C) oven for 30 minutes; uncover, and bake for about 20 minutes or until golden brown and potatoes are tender.

Makes 6 servings.
PREPARATION: *15 minutes*
COOK: *50 minutes*

Each serving: ⅔ cup (150 mL)

1 ▢ Starchy Choice
1 ▲ Fats & Oils Choice

20 g carbohydrate, 3 g protein, 5 g fat, 2 g fibre, 130 kcal (540 kJ)

KITCHEN TIP

When cooking scalloped potatoes with a roast, cook in 325°F (160°C) oven and increase cooking time by about 15 minutes.

STRAWBERRY YOGURT DESSERT

This creamy and delicious dessert has a fraction of the calories of one made with whipped cream.

2 tbsp	water	25 mL
1 tbsp	granulated sugar	15 mL
3 cups	sliced strawberries, divided	750 mL
¾ cup	low-fat plain yogurt	175 mL
¼ tsp	almond extract	1 mL

• In microwaveable bowl, microwave water and sugar on High (100%) for 1 minute or until sugar is dissolved. Stir in 1 cup (250 mL) strawberries. Microwave for 1 to 2 minutes; mash and cool.
• Just before serving, stir in remaining strawberries, yogurt and almond extract.

Makes 5 servings, 2½ cups (625 mL).
PREPARATION: 10 minutes
COOK: 2 to 3 minutes

Each serving: ½ cup (125 mL)

1 ◪ Fruits & Vegetables Choice

11 g carbohydrate, 3 g protein, 1 g fat, 2 g fibre, 60 kcal (250 kJ)

CHICKEN AND MUSHROOM BURGERS

Barbecued or oven-broiled, these burgers will be a hit with the entire family. Make extra patties and freeze them for busy-day meals.

1 lb	lean ground chicken	500 g
1 cup	finely chopped mushrooms (5 to 6 large)	250 mL
½ cup	chopped onion	125 mL
1	clove garlic, minced	1
¼ cup	fine dried breadcrumbs	50 mL
1 tsp	dried tarragon	5 mL
¼ tsp	dried thyme	1 mL
¼ tsp	salt	1 mL
¼ tsp	pepper	1 mL
6	whole wheat buns	6

• In bowl, combine chicken, mushrooms, onion, garlic, breadcrumbs and seasonings. Shape into 6 patties, about ½-inch (1 cm) thick.
• Broil or barbecue for 5 to 6 minutes per side or until brown and chicken is cooked through. Serve on whole wheat buns with garnishes. Suggested garnishes are: light mayonnaise, tomato slices, alfalfa sprouts or lettuce, mustard.

Makes 6 burgers.
PREPARATION: 10 minutes
COOK: 10 to 12 minutes

Each serving: 1 patty and bun

2 ◻ Starchy Choices
2½ ◪ Protein Choices

31 g carbohydrate, 22 g protein, 6 g fat, 3 g fibre, 258 kcal (1080 kJ)

KITCHEN TIPS

• Always cook poultry until well done. When poultry is cooked properly, all juices from the meat are clear, not pink.
• Hamburger buns vary widely in size. We used an average package of 8 supermarket hamburger buns for these burgers.

SPINACH AND ORANGE SALAD

This perfect buffet salad doesn't require too much preparation.

1	pkg (10 oz/284 g) fresh spinach	1
3	medium oranges, peeled and sectioned	3
½	red onion, sliced	½

Dressing:

⅓ cup	raspberry vinegar*	75 mL
¼ cup	vegetable oil	50 mL
1 tbsp	liquid calorie-free sweetener	15 mL
1 tsp	poppy seeds	5 mL
¼ tsp	salt	1 mL
	Freshly ground pepper	

Salad
• Wash and dry spinach. Remove stems and tear leaves into bite-sized pieces.
• In large salad bowl, combine spinach, oranges and red onion. Cover and refrigerate for at least 30 minutes before serving.

Dressing
• In a container with a tight-fitting lid, combine vinegar, oil, sweetener and seasonings; shake well and refrigerate. Pour over salad and toss lightly just before serving.

Makes 12 servings, 12 cups (3 L).
PREPARATION: *15 minutes*
CHILL: *about 30 minutes or longer*

Each serving: 1 cup (250 mL) salad with dressing

½ ▱ Fruits & Vegetables Choice
1 ▲ Fats & Oils Choice

*7 g carbohydrate, 1 g protein, 5 g fat,
2 g fibre, 70 kcal (290 kJ)*

TOMATO ZUCCHINI BAKE

Frequently the easiest recipes are the best. This one is an excellent use of summer's garden vegetables.

2	medium tomatoes, sliced	2
1	medium zucchini, thinly sliced	1
1	green onion, sliced	1
2 tbsp	grated Parmesan cheese	25 mL
¼ tsp	salt	1 mL
¼ tsp	freshly ground pepper	1 mL
¼ tsp	dried oregano	1 mL

• In a shallow casserole, layer tomato and zucchini slices in an overlapping circle. Top with green onion; sprinkle with cheese, salt, pepper and oregano.
• Bake in 350°F (180°C) oven for about 20 minutes or until vegetables are just tender.

Makes 4 servings.
PREPARATION: *10 minutes*
COOK: *15 minutes*

Each serving: ¼ of recipe

½ ▱ Fruits & Vegetables Choice
1 ▨ Extra

*5 g carbohydrate, 2 g protein, 1 g fat,
2 g fibre, 34 kcal (140 kJ)*

KITCHEN TIP

*To make your own raspberry vinegar, add 3 cups (750 mL) fresh or frozen raspberries to 1½ cups (375 mL) white wine vinegar. Allow to stand at room temperature for several days. Strain and pour into clean sealed bottles. Makes about 2 cups (500 mL) vinegar.

LIGHT'N' EASY CHEESECAKE WITH FRESH FRUIT

The whole family will enjoy this dessert. Bake it a few hours ahead and chill.

Crust

¾ cup	gingersnap cookie crumbs	175 mL
	(seven 2½-inch/6 cm cookies)	
2 tbsp	melted margarine or butter	25 mL

Filling

1	container (500 g) low-fat	1
	cottage cheese	
½	pkg (250 g) light cream cheese	½
2	egg whites	2
2 tbsp	granulated sugar	25 mL
2 tbsp	all purpose flour	25 mL
½ tsp	orange rind	2 mL
¼ tsp	orange **or** lemon extract	1 mL
	8 sliced strawberries and/or	
	2 kiwifruit, mint leaves for garnish	

Crust

• Spray an 8-inch (20 cm) springform pan with nonstick coating.
• Blend cookie crumbs and melted margarine. Press into bottom of pan. Bake in 350°F (180°C) oven for 8 minutes.

Filling

• In food processor or blender, blend cottage cheese, cream cheese, egg whites, sugar, flour, orange rind and orange or lemon extract until very smooth; pour over crust.
• Bake in 350°F (180°C) oven for about 45 minutes or until knife inserted in centre comes out clean. Loosen edges of cheesecake with a knife; cool on rack.
• Chill 2 to 3 hours before serving. Garnish with fresh strawberries, sliced kiwifruit and mint leaves.

Makes 8 servings.
PREPARATION: 20 minutes
COOK: 45 minutes
CHILL: 2 to 3 hours

Each serving: ⅛ of cheescake

½ ☐ Starchy Choice
1 ▨ Fruits & Vegetables Choice
1½ ▨ Protein Choices
1 ▲ Fats & Oils Choice

*20 g carbohydrate, 12 g protein, 9 g fat,
1 g fibre, 203 kcal (850 kJ)*

CHICKEN CACCIATORE

This is a favourite old world Italian casserole recipe. Your extra Vegetable Spaghetti Sauce allows you to whip up this extremely easy dinner at the last moment.

4	small chicken legs (about 1¼ lb/600 g)	4
1 tbsp	vegetable oil	15 mL
2 cups	**Vegetable Spaghetti Sauce**	500 mL
	(*page 86*)	
½	green pepper, cut into strips	½
1 cup	chopped onion	250 mL

• Remove and discard skin and fat from chicken.
• In large skillet, heat oil on medium-high heat; add chicken and sauté until brown. Transfer chicken to a shallow casserole.
• Combine spaghetti sauce with green pepper and onion. Spoon sauce over chicken.
• Cover and bake in 400°F (200°C) oven for 45 to 55 minutes or until chicken is tender.

Makes 4 servings.
PREPARATION: 15 minutes if Vegetable Spaghetti Sauce is prepared
COOK: 45 to 55 minutes

Each serving: ¼ of recipe

1 ▨ Fruits & Vegetables Choice
2½ ▨ Protein Choices
½ ▲ Fats & Oils Choice

*11 g carbohydrate, 19 g protein, 10 g fat,
3 g fibre, 205 kcal (860 kJ)*

SNACKS

Snacks are not for everyone! Unplanned snacks can defeat all your weight control efforts and leave you with the "guilts."

However, planned snacks can help you avoid that between-meal slump that happens when there is more than four or five hours between meals. With a planned snack, you are less hungry at the next meal and less inclined to overeat.

Your meal plan determines how much snacking you can do.

• The 1200-calorie plan does not allow any planned added snacks. However, you can save food from a meal to have as a snack later. Small but frequent meals are fine and help you control the hunger pangs.

• The 1500-calorie plan allows two 150-calorie snacks or one 300-calorie snack each day.

• The 1800-calorie plan allows two 150-calorie snacks *and* one 300-calorie snack each day.

When you have your snacks is up to you. Just remember to space them over the day.

SNACK RECIPES INDEX

Another use for Multimix! These scones are cut into the traditional Scottish wedges.

2 cups	**Multimix** (*page 54*)	500 mL
2 tbsp	dried currants or raisins	25 mL
1 tbsp	granulated sugar	15 mL
½ cup	buttermilk or sour milk*	125 mL
1	egg, beaten	1
1 tsp	grated orange rind (optional)	5 mL
2 tbsp	all purpose flour	25 mL

• In medium bowl, combine Multimix, currants and sugar.

• In second bowl, stir together buttermilk, egg and orange rind. Pour into dry mixture; stir with fork until dry ingredients are just moistened.

• Turn dough out onto board lightly dusted with 2 tbsp (25 mL) flour; knead gently about 20 times. Divide in two. Pat each piece into 6-inch (15 cm) round, about ½-inch (1 cm) thick. Transfer to ungreased baking sheet; cut each round into 6 triangles.

• Bake in 375°F (190°C) oven for about 20 minutes or until lightly browned.

Makes 12 scones.
PREPARATION: 15 minutes
COOK: about 20 minutes

Each serving: 1 scone (¹/₁₂ of recipe)

1 ☐ Starchy Choice
1 ▲ Fats & Oils Choice

*15 g carbohydrate, 3 g protein, 6 g fat,
1 g fibre, 118 kcal (490 kJ)*

. . . .
KITCHEN TIP

*If you don't have buttermilk, stir 1 tsp (5 mL) lemon juice or vinegar into ½ cup (125 mL) milk; let stand for 5 minutes.

Cottage cheese with a difference! Keep this handy snacking spread in the refrigerator for up to one week.

1 cup	low-fat cottage cheese	250 mL
1 tbsp	light mayonnaise	15 mL
1 tbsp	cider vinegar	15 mL
2 tbsp	finely chopped parsley or cilantro	25 mL
1	green onion, finely chopped	1
½ tsp	dried dillweed	2 mL
½ tsp	Dijon mustard	2 mL
¼ tsp	salt	1 mL
Dash	hot pepper sauce	Dash

• In blender or food processor, combine cottage cheese, mayonnaise and vinegar; process until smooth. Remove to bowl and stir in parsley, onion and seasonings.

• Cover and refrigerate for at least 1 hour to allow flavours to develop. Keep for up to one week in the refrigerator, or freeze for longer storage.

Makes 5 servings, 1¼ cups (300 mL).
PREPARATION: 10 minutes
CHILL: 1 hour

Each serving: ¼ cup (50 mL)

1 ◪ Protein Choice

*2 g carbohydrate, 6 g protein, 2 g fat,
0 g fibre, 52 kcal (220 kJ)*

---

or for a smaller portion:

Each serving: 2 tbsp (25 mL)

½ ◪ Protein Choice

*1 g carbohydrate, 3 g protein, 1 g fat,
0 g fibre, 26 kcal (110 kJ)*

. . . .
KITCHEN TIP

Great as a topping for baked potato.

SNACK SCRAMBLE

A nibble to enjoy in the evening with cards or the news.

3 cups	small shredded wheat squares	750 mL
3 cups	O-shaped toasted oat cereal	750 mL
2 cups	slim pretzels	500 mL
1 cup	peanuts	250 mL
1/4 cup	melted margarine or butter	50 mL
1 tbsp	Worcestershire sauce	15 mL
1 tsp	seasoned salt	5 mL
1/2 tsp	garlic powder	2 mL
Dash	hot pepper sauce	Dash

• In large bowl, combine cereals, pretzels and peanuts. Stir together melted margarine and seasonings. Pour over cereal mixture and toss to coat well.
• Place mixture on large baking pan or roaster and bake in 250°F (120°C) oven for about 45 minutes; stir every 15 minutes.

Makes 18 servings, 9 cups (2.25 L).
PREPARATION: *10 minutes*
COOK: *45 minutes*

Each serving: ½ cup (125 mL)

1 ☐ Starchy Choice
1 ▲ Fats & Oils Choice

*16 g carbohydrate, 3 g protein, 6 g fat,
2 g fibre, 123 kcal (520 kJ)*

MULTIMIX TEA BISCUITS

Fast and easy to make with Multimix, these biscuits may be used for fruit shortcake *(see Dinner Menu #24)* or as a snack with a cup of tea.

2/3 cup	skim milk	150 mL
2 cups	**Multimix** *(page 54)*	500 mL
1 tbsp	all purpose flour	15 mL

• In bowl, stir milk into Multimix with a fork just until dry ingredients are combined.
• Turn out onto board lightly dusted with 1 tbsp (15 mL) flour; knead dough 20 times or until smooth. Roll dough to ½-inch (1 cm) thick. Cut 12 rounds with floured 2-inch (5 cm) biscuit cutter. Transfer to ungreased baking sheet.
• Bake in 425°F (220°C) oven for about 12 minutes or until lightly browned.

Makes 12 biscuits.
PREPARATION: *10 minutes*
COOK: *about 12 minutes*

Each serving: 1 biscuit (1/12 of recipe)

1 ☐ Starchy Choice
1 ▲ Fats & Oils Choice

*12 g carbohydrate, 2 g protein, 5 g fat,
1 g fibre, 101 kcal (420 kJ)*

CORNMEAL MUFFINS

Cornmeal provides a special flavour to baked goods. When you want a savoury muffin, use dried herbs; for a snack muffin to enjoy with tea, use grated orange rind.

1 ¼ cups	low-fat milk	300 mL
1 cup	cornmeal	250 mL
⅓ cup	melted margarine or butter	75 mL
1	egg, beaten	1
1 cup	all purpose flour	250 mL
3 tbsp	granulated sugar	45 mL
1 tbsp	baking powder	15 mL
1 tsp	Italian herbs **or** grated orange rind	5 mL
¼ tsp	salt	1 mL

• In medium bowl, stir together milk and cornmeal; let stand for 5 minutes. Stir in melted margarine and egg.
• In second bowl, combine flour, sugar, baking powder, herbs or orange rind and salt. Add to cornmeal mixture; stir just until combined.
• Spoon batter into 12 lightly greased or paper-lined medium muffin cups.
• Bake in 375°F (190°C) oven for about 18 minutes or until firm to touch.

Makes 12 medium muffins.
PREPARATION: 10 minutes
COOK: about 18 minutes

Each serving: 1 muffin (¹⁄₁₂ of recipe)

1 ☐ Starchy Choice
½ ◪ Fruits & Vegetables Choice
1 ▲ Fats & Oils Choice

*22 g carbohydrate, 4 g protein, 5 g fat,
1 g fibre, 148 kcal (620 kJ)*

OLD-FASHIONED JAM COOKIES

Cookies like Grandma used to make! Another good use for one of the Fruit Spreads from the Breakfast section *(see page 55)*.

½ cup	margarine or butter	125 mL
¼ cup	granulated sugar	50 mL
1	egg yolk	1
2 tsp	lemon juice	10 mL
1 cup	all purpose flour	250 mL
5 tbsp	Fruit Spread *(page 55)*	60 mL

• In medium bowl, cream margarine and sugar until light. Beat in egg yolk and lemon juice. Stir in flour until well blended.
• Shape dough into 1-inch (2.5 cm) balls; place on ungreased baking sheet. Press a small indentation into centre of each ball.
• Bake in 350°F (180°C) oven for about 12 minutes. Cool. Spoon ½ tsp (2 mL) Fruit Spread in each indentation at serving time.

Makes 30 cookies.
PREPARATION: 15 minutes
COOK: 12 minutes

Each serving: 3 cookies.

1 ☐ Starchy Choice
1½ ▲ Fats & Oils Choices

*15 g carbohydrate, 2 g protein, 7 g fat,
1 g fibre, 132 kcal (540 kJ)*

KITCHEN TIP

Freeze these cookies without Fruit Spread.

YOGURT FRUIT SHAKE

Enjoy this thick, creamy blender shake for a snack between meals.

1 cup	low-fat plain yogurt	250 mL
1	medium banana, peeled, cut up and frozen	1
½ cup	chopped strawberries (about 3 large)	125 mL
1 tsp	granulated sugar	5 mL

• In food processor or blender, combine yogurt, frozen banana, strawberries and sugar. Blend for 1 minute or until smooth.

Makes 2 servings, 1½ cups (375 mL).
PREPARATION: 5 minutes

Each serving: ¾ cup (175 mL)

1½ ◪ Fruits & Vegetables Choices
1½ ◧ 2% Milk Choices

*25 g carbohydrate, 7 g protein, 2 g fat,
2 g fibre, 140 kcal (590 kJ)*

KITCHEN TIPS

• Freeze Hummus in small amounts for later use, for dipping or as a sandwich spread.
• Since flour tortillas come in packages of 10 or 12, bake extra snackers and keep in tightly closed container.

HUMMUS DIP WITH TORTILLA SNACKERS

A high-fibre vegetarian dip of Middle Eastern origin. When served with tortillas, the bread of Mexico, East meets West!

Hummus

1	can (19 oz/540 mL) chick peas, drained	1
1 to 2	cloves garlic, minced	1 to 2
½ cup	low-fat plain yogurt	125 mL
3 tbsp	lemon juice	45 mL
½ tsp	salt	2 mL
½ tsp	ground cumin	2 mL
Dash	hot pepper sauce	Dash
	Freshly ground pepper	

Tortilla Snackers

4	8-inch (20 cm) flour tortillas	4

Hummus
• In food processor or blender, purée chick peas with garlic until coarsely chopped. Add yogurt, lemon juice and seasonings; blend to smooth paste.
• Remove and refrigerate, covered, for at least 2 hours so flavours develop.

Tortilla Snackers
• Cut each tortilla with scissors into 12 triangles. Place in single layer on baking pan. Bake in 300°F (160°C) oven for 15 to 20 minutes or until crisp and golden. Allow snackers to cool; store in tightly closed container.

Makes 48 tortilla snackers and 2⅓ cups (575 mL) hummus.
PREPARATION: 10 minutes
CHILL: 2 hours or longer

Each serving: ⅓ cup (75 mL) Hummus with 6 Tortilla Snackers

1½ ▢ Starchy Choices
1 ▨ Protein Choice

*28 g carbohydrate, 7 g protein, 3 g fat,
4 g fibre, 162 kcal (680 kJ)*

OATMEAL SODA BREAD

Scottish oats added to Irish Soda Bread make this snack a source of soluble fibre.

1½ cups	all purpose flour	375 mL
1 cup	quick cooking rolled oats	250 mL
1½ tsp	baking powder	7 mL
½ tsp	baking soda	2 mL
½ tsp	salt	2 mL
1 tbsp	granulated sugar	15 mL
¼ cup	currants	50 mL
1 cup	buttermilk	250 mL
2 tbsp	melted margarine or butter	25 mL
1	egg, beaten	1
1 tbsp	milk	15 mL
2 tbsp	quick cooking rolled oats	25 mL

• In large bowl, combine flour, 1 cup (250 mL) rolled oats, baking powder, baking soda, salt, sugar and currants.
• In second bowl, stir together buttermilk, margarine and egg. Stir into dry ingredients just until moistened.
• Turn out onto lightly floured board; knead dough 10 times or until smooth. Pat into lightly greased 8-inch (20 cm) round cake pan. Cut deep cross in top, brush with milk and sprinkle with 2 tbsp (25 mL) rolled oats.
• Bake in 375°F (190°C) oven for 30 minutes or until tester inserted in centre comes out clean and bread is golden brown. Cool on wire rack for 5 minutes before removing from pan. Cut into 8 wedges.

Makes 8 servings.
PREPARATION: 15 minutes
COOK: 30 minutes

Each serving: 1 wedge (⅛ of recipe)
2 ☐ Starchy Choices
1 ▲ Fats & Oils Choice
35 g carbohydrate, 7 g protein, 5 g fat, 2 g fibre, 209 kcal (870 kJ)

QUICK CHEESE TOASTS

Alone or served with soup, these toasts are delicious. Make the spread ahead and keep tightly covered in the refrigerator ready for a quick snack. It keeps for several weeks.

1 cup	freshly grated Parmesan cheese	250 mL
½ cup	light mayonnaise	125 mL
¼ tsp	garlic powder (optional) **or**	1 mL
	1 clove garlic, minced	
	French or Italian bread*	

• In bowl, mix cheese, mayonnaise and garlic, if using. Refrigerate spread in tightly sealed container until ready to use.
• Spread cheese mixture on sliced bread (for directions, see Kitchen Tip below).
• Place bread on baking sheet; broil for 1 to 2 minutes or until cheese bubbles and becomes golden brown. Serve hot.

Makes 1½ cups (375 mL) spread.
PREPARATION: 5 minutes
COOK: 1 to 2 minutes

Each serving: 4 slices bread with 4 tsp (20 mL) spread
1 ☐ Starchy Choice
1 ▲ Fats & Oils Choice
15 g carbohydrate, 4 g protein, 4 g fat, 0 g fibre, 109 kcal (460 kJ)

KITCHEN TIP

*If using long, thin French bread stick, cut 4 slices bread ¼-inch (5 mm) thick for each serving. Slice, label and freeze extra French bread stick.

If using white or whole wheat bread, cut each slice into 4 squares.

CURRIED CHEDDAR SPREAD

Serve this "nippy" spread with crackers as a snack when planning a delayed meal.

1½ cups	shredded light Cheddar cheese	375 mL
½ cup	light cream cheese (one-half of a 250 g pkg)	125 mL
½ cup	light mayonnaise	125 mL
2 tbsp	fruit chutney	25 mL
2 tsp	horseradish	10 mL
1 tsp	curry powder	5 mL
½ tsp	Worcestershire sauce	2 mL
Pinch	cayenne pepper	Pinch
¼ cup	chopped parsley	50 mL
2 tbsp	finely chopped onion	25 mL

• In food processor or blender, combine Cheddar cheese, cream cheese, mayonnaise, chutney, horseradish and seasonings; process until smooth. Remove to bowl and stir in parsley and onion.
• Refrigerate in tightly sealed container for up to one week or freeze for longer storage.

Makes about 10 servings, 2 cups (500 mL).
PREPARATION: 15 minutes

Each serving: 3 tbsp (45 mL)

1 ☑ Protein Choice
1 ▲ Fats & Oils Choice
1 ▣ Extra

*3 g carbohydrate, 6 g protein, 10 g fat,
0 g fibre, 117 kcal (490 kJ)*

KITCHEN TIP

Line a bowl or mold with plastic wrap; pack the spread in the lined bowl, cover and refrigerate until firm. Cut into smaller pieces and freeze for longer storage.

ORANGE PRUNE SNACKING BREAD

Orange and prune flavours are delicious at breakfast as well as at snack time. Serve fruit bread slices with milk, tea or coffee.

2½ cups	all purpose flour	625 mL
⅓ cup	granulated sugar	75 mL
2 tsp	baking powder	10 mL
½ tsp	baking soda	2 mL
½ tsp	ground ginger	2 mL
1 cup	skim milk	250 mL
½ cup	frozen orange juice concentrate	125 mL
2	eggs	2
¼ cup	vegetable oil	50 mL
½ cup	finely chopped dried prunes (10 pitted)	125 mL

• In large bowl, combine flour, sugar, baking powder, baking soda and ginger.
• In second bowl, stir together milk, juice concentrate, eggs and oil. Stir into dry ingredients just until moistened. Stir in prunes. Spoon into 9x5-inch (2 L) lightly greased loaf pan.
• Bake in 350°F (180°C) oven for about 50 minutes or until cake tester inserted in centre comes out clean.
• Cool for 10 minutes before removing from pan to wire rack to cool completely.

Makes 16 slices.
PREPARATION: 15 minutes
COOK: about 50 minutes

Each serving: 1 slice (1/16 of recipe)

1 ☐ Starchy Choice
1 ☑ Fruits & Vegetables Choice
1 ▲ Fats & Oils Choice

*28 g carbohydrate, 4 g protein, 5 g fat,
2 g fibre, 167 kcal (700 kJ)*

SPECIAL OCCASIONS

Special occasions usually mean large groups, small gatherings, seasonal events, birthdays, holidays. They often include special meals that are a temptation and a problem for the person trying to keep to a diet.
Here are eight additional complete menus to use for special events. Recipes and menus have been planned for four, six, eight and twelve people.

We certainly want you to enjoy social events. You want to eat the same food as everyone else. Delayed meals can be a problem if you take pills or insulin for your diabetes. Plan to eat a snack at your usual meal time. Then you can wait comfortably until the meal is served.

Should you be planning to entertain someone who has diabetes, we believe these menus will make things easier. Just remember, serving sizes are important. Menus describe clearly the amounts for 1 serving. Let others eat the amounts they want.

SPECIAL OCCASION MENUS

Menu #1
Evening Buffet for Six or Twelve

Menu #2
Weekend Brunch

Menu #3
A Spring Dinner for Six

Menu #4
Gourmet Dinner for Four

Menu #5
Backyard Barbecue

Menu #6
A Summer Picnic

Menu #7
Thanksgiving Dinner for Four or Eight

Menu #8
Holiday Dinner for Eight

Menu #2 is about 500 calories (similar to a lunch menu). All other menus are about 500 to 600 calories (based on dinner menus).

Beverages for Special Occasions

Beverages are a part of most social occasions. The following non-alcoholic drinks are low in calories, and can be considered free foods or "extras."

- soda water or club soda, with lime or lemon
- mineral water, plain or flavoured (unsweetened)
- diet soft drinks
- water, tea, coffee

ALCOHOLIC BEVERAGES: Alcohol also has its place, used with discretion. The following table gives some guidance for its use. Alcohol provides 7 calories per gram.

DRINK	CARBOHYDRATE	ALCOHOL	CALORIES
dry white wine (6 oz / 175 mL)	—	16 g	110
dry red wine (6 oz / 175 mL)	—	16 g	110
dry sherry (2 oz / 60 mL)	—	9 g	63
brandy or cognac (1½ oz / 45 mL)	—	15 g	105
rye, Scotch whiskey, gin, rum, vodka (1½ oz / 45 mL)	—	15 g	105
regular beer (12 oz / 355 mL)	10 to 13 g	15 g	150
light beer (12 oz / 355 mL)	10 g	11 g	100
non-alcoholic beer 0.5% (12 oz / 355 mL)	12 to 18 g	2 g	60 to 85

IMPORTANT:

- Check with your doctor before drinking alcohol; it should not be consumed with some oral medications.

- Limit yourself to one, or at the most two drinks on an occasion.

EVENING BUFFET FOR SIX OR TWELVE
(with amounts for one serving)

1 slice **Bruschetta Appetizer** *(page 114)*

assorted crisp raw vegetables
(broccoli and cauliflower florets, cucumber slices, celery and zucchini sticks, cherry tomatoes, green and red pepper slices)
with 3 tbsp (45 mL) **Creamy Herb Dip** *(page 74)*

1 cup (250 mL) **Wild Rice Turkey Casserole** *(page 115)*

½ cup (125 mL) **Spiced Beets** *(page 114)*

1 cup (250 mL) **Spinach and Orange Salad** *(page 97)*

⅛ **Snowball Dessert** with 3 tbsp (45 mL) **Raspberry Sauce** *(page 116)*

tea or coffee

WEEKEND BRUNCH
(with amounts for one serving)

½ cup (125 mL) **Fruit Bowl Ambrosia** *(page 117)*

⅙ **Broccoli and Ham Strata** *(page 117)*

1 **Banana Muffin** *(page 57)* or
1 **Raisin Bran Buttermilk Muffin** *(page 61)*

tea or coffee

3

A SPRING DINNER FOR SIX
(with amounts for one serving)

3 slices (90 g) roast leg of lamb with mint sauce
mint leaves and vinegar, sweetener if desired

⅙ **Roasted Potato Slices** *(page 90)*

6 steamed asparagus tips

⅙ **Cucumber and Orange Salad** *(page 118)*

1 cup (250 mL) Fresh Fruit Cocktail with Lime
*½ cup (125 mL) honeydew melon balls and ½ cup (125 mL) sliced strawberries,
sprinkled with 1 tsp (5 mL) lime juice, rind and sweetener*

tea or coffee

4

GOURMET DINNER FOR FOUR
(with amounts for one serving)

1 cup (250 mL) **Rhubarb Punch** *(page 118)*
⅓ cup (75 mL) concentrate with soda water and ice

1 **Poached Chicken Breast** with
3 tbsp (45 mL) **Cranberry Coulis** *(page 119)*

½ cup (125 mL) **Barley Pilaf** *(page 120)*

½ cup (125 mL) Green Beans Amandine
sprinkle with 1 tsp (5 mL) toasted slivered almonds

⅙ **Favourite Caesar Salad** *(page 75)*

Strawberry Shortcake with Whipped Cream
*½ Multimix Tea Biscuit (page 101), 1 cup (250 mL) fresh or frozen strawberries, and
2 tbsp (25 mL) whipped cream, sweetened, if desired, with 1 tsp (5 mL) liqueur*

tea or coffee

BACKYARD BARBECUE
(with amounts for one serving)

1 (100 g raw) barbecued bratwurst sausage
with Dijon mustard

corn on the cob
one cob (10-inch/24 cm long) **or** *two cobs (each 5-inch/12 cm long)*
with ½ tsp (2 mL) margarine or butter

sliced tomatoes

Fresh Peach Sundae
½ large peach sliced over ⅓ cup (75 mL) light ice cream (7% BF)

iced lemonade with sweetener

5

A SUMMER PICNIC
(with amounts for one serving)

2 pieces **Crispy Baked Chicken** *(page 91)*

½ cup (125 mL) **Summertime Potato Salad** *(page 83)*

½ cup (125 mL) coleslaw with oil and vinegar dressing

assorted raw vegetables
celery sticks, zucchini sticks, cucumber slices, green onions, radishes, cherry tomatoes
with ⅓ cup (75 mL) **Creamy Herb Dip** *(page 74)*

1 slice watermelon (5-inch/12 cm wedge, 1-inch/2.5 cm thick)
or
1 large peach

fruit-flavoured sugar-free mineral water

6

7

THANKSGIVING DINNER FOR FOUR OR EIGHT
(with amounts for one serving)

1 cup (250 mL) **Golden Harvest Soup** *(page 120)*

½ **Cornish Hen with Wild Rice Dressing** *(page 121)*

½ cup (125 mL) steamed broccoli and cauliflower with lemon wedge

½ cup (125 mL) carrot coins

mixed salad greens
Boston and iceberg lettuce, romaine, radicchio
with 2 tbsp (25 mL) **Herb Vinaigrette Dressing** *(page 81)*

⅛ **Spicy Pumpkin Pie** *(page 122)*
with 2 tbsp (25 mL) light vanilla ice cream (7% BF)

tea or coffee

8

HOLIDAY DINNER FOR EIGHT
(with amounts for one serving)

1 cup (250 mL) consommé with chopped parsley

3 slices (90 g) roast turkey
⅔ cup (150 mL) **Poultry Dressing** *(page 82)*
¼ cup (50 mL) **Light Gravy** *(page 82)*

½ cup (125 mL) mashed potatoes

1 cup (250 mL) French-style green beans

½ cup (125 mL) **Braised Red Cabbage with Cranberries** *(page 123)*

Festive Raspberry Parfait
3 tbsp (45 mL) Raspberry Sauce (page 116) over ⅓ cup (75 mL) light vanilla ice cream (7% BF)

tea or coffee

SPECIAL OCCASIONS RECIPES INDEX

BRUSCHETTA APPETIZER

Top thick slices of toasted Italian bread with ruby cubes of tomatoes flavoured with garlic, basil and Parmesan cheese.

3	slices Italian bread, ¾-inch (2 cm) thick	3
¾ cup	finely chopped fresh tomato (1 medium)	175 mL
1 tsp	grated Parmesan cheese	5 mL
1 tsp	olive oil	5 mL
½ tsp	dried basil **or**	2 mL
2 tsp	chopped fresh basil	10 mL
1	small clove garlic, minced	1

• Broil or toast bread on each side until golden brown.
• In small bowl, mix chopped tomato, Parmesan cheese, oil, basil and garlic. Spoon ¼ cup (50 mL) tomato mixture onto each slice of toast. Return to broiler for 2 to 3 minutes to warm slightly.

Makes 3 servings.
PREPARATION: *10 minutes*
COOK: *about 5 minutes*

Each serving: 1 slice

1 ☐ Starchy Choice
½ ▲ Fats & Oils Choice

16 g carbohydrate, 3 g protein, 2 g fat, 1 g fibre, 95 kcal (400 kJ)

SPICED BEETS

Mildly spiced, this vegetable dish will remind you of pickled beets. An attractive addition to your buffet table.

2	cans (14 oz/398 mL) sliced beets **or**	2
1½ cups	diced cooked beets	375 mL
½ cup	water, optional	125 mL
½ cup	chopped onion	125 mL
¼ cup	cider vinegar	50 mL
¼ tsp	salt	1 mL
¼ tsp	ground cloves	1 mL
¼ tsp	pepper	1 mL
½ cup	finely minced parsley	125 mL

• Drain beets; reserve ½ cup (125 mL) beet liquid. Dice beets.
• In saucepan, bring beet liquid or water, onion, vinegar and seasonings to boil. Add beets, cover, and cook for about 5 minutes or until beets are heated through and onion is tender. Sprinkle with parsley and serve.

Makes 6 servings, 3 cups (750 mL).
PREPARATION: *10 minutes*
COOK: *about 5 minutes*

Each serving: ½ cup (125 mL)

½ ▱ Fruits & Vegetables Choice

7 g carbohydrate, 1 g protein, 0 g fat, 2 g fibre, 32 kcal (130 kJ)

WILD RICE
TURKEY CASSEROLE

Cubed cooked turkey or chicken is ideal in recipes for entertaining. For a crowd, prepare the casseroles ahead. This recipe makes two casseroles for 12 people, but you can easily freeze the second casserole and serve only 6 people at each meal.

1/2 cup	wild rice	125 mL
1/3 cup	long grain white rice	75 mL
1	can (10 oz/284 mL) water chestnuts, drained and sliced	1
4 cups	large cubes of cooked turkey meat (white and dark)	1 L
1 tbsp	margarine or butter	15 mL
2 cups	sliced mushrooms	500 mL
1 cup	chopped onion (1 medium)	250 mL
1 cup	chopped sweet red pepper	250 mL
2 cups	chicken broth	500 mL
2 tbsp	all purpose flour	25 mL
1 tsp	salt	5 mL
1 tsp	poultry seasoning	5 mL
1/2 tsp	pepper	2 mL
1/2 cup	slivered toasted almonds	125 mL

• In separate saucepans, cook wild rice and white rice according to package directions or until rices are tender; combine. Stir water chestnuts and turkey into rice. Set aside.
• In large skillet melt margarine over medium-high heat. Add mushrooms, onion and red pepper; cook for 5 minutes. Stir into rice mixture.
• Whisk together broth, flour, seasonings and 1/4 cup (50 mL) water. Cook over medium heat for 5 minutes or until slightly thickened; stir constantly. Stir into rice mixture. Divide between two 6-cup (1.5 L) casseroles.*
• Cover casseroles. Bake in 350°F (180°C) oven for 30 to 40 minutes or until heated.
• Sprinkle each 1 cup (250 mL) serving with 2 tsp (10 mL) toasted almonds.

Makes 12 servings, 12 cups (3 L).
PREPARATION: 45 minutes
COOK: 30 to 40 minutes

Each serving: 1 cup (250 mL)

1 ☐ Starchy Choice
2 ☑ Protein Choices

17 g carbohydrate, 17 g protein, 7 g fat, 2 g fibre, 191 kcal (800 kJ)

KITCHEN TIPS

• *If only one casserole is required, seal second casserole securely with aluminum foil, label well and freeze.
• If you do not have cooked meat, purchase 1 turkey breast or 1 small turkey roast. Bake according to package directions, cool and cube.

SNOWBALL DESSERT WITH RASPBERRY SAUCE

When entertaining six people at your Evening Buffet Dinner, make one snowball. If entertaining 12, make two *(see Menu #1)*. This recipe makes eight servings We're assuming some of your guests will be coming back for more!

Snowball Dessert

2	envelopes (7g each) unflavoured gelatin	2
3 tbsp	granulated white low-calorie sweetener, divided	45 mL
2 tbsp	granulated sugar	25 mL
2 cups	low-fat milk	500 mL
2	eggs, separated	2
1 cup	light (7%) sour cream	250 mL
1	pkg (250 g) skim-milk (0.3%) pressed cottage cheese	1
2 tsp	vanilla extract	10 mL

Raspberry Sauce

1	pkg (300g) frozen unsweetened raspberries	1
1 tbsp	cornstarch	15 mL
2 tbsp	granulated white low-calorie sweetener	25 mL
1/2 tsp	almond or orange extract	2 mL

Snowball

• In saucepan, combine gelatin, 2 tbsp (25 mL) sweetener, sugar and milk. Beat egg yolks; stir into milk mixture. Cook over medium heat, stirring constantly, until mixture is thick enough to coat a metal spoon. Remove from heat and cool slightly.
• Beat in sour cream, cottage cheese and vanilla with electric beater; refrigerate for about 45 minutes or until slightly thickened.
• Beat egg whites with remaining sweetener until soft peaks form. Fold into gelatin mixture; pour into 6-cup (1.5 mL) mold or bowl. Cover and refrigerate for 2 hours or until firm.

Makes 8 servings, one snowball.
PREPARATION: 30 minutes
CHILL: 2 hours or longer

Raspberry Sauce

• In saucepan, cook raspberries and 1/4 cup (50 mL) water, covered, until raspberries are thawed and mixture comes to a boil.
• Combine cornstarch, sweetener and 1/4 cup (50 mL) water; stir into raspberry mixture and cook until sauce thickens. Stir in almond extract. Cover and refrigerate for at least 30 minutes.

Makes 1 1/2 cups (375 mL) sauce.
PREPARATION: 10 minutes
CHILL: 30 minutes

Each serving: 1/8 of snowball with 3 tbsp (45 mL) raspberry sauce

1 ◪ Fruits & Vegetables Choice
1/2 ◆ 2% Milk Choice
1 1/2 ◪ Protein Choices

16 g carbohydrate, 13 g protein, 5 g fat, 2 g fibre, 157 kcal (660 kJ)

Raspberry Sauce alone:

Each serving: 3 tbsp (45 mL)

1/2 ◪ Fruits & Vegetables Choice

6 g carbohydrate, 0 g protein, 0 g fat, 2 g fibre, 23 kcal (96 kJ)

FRUIT BOWL AMBROSIA

Fresh seasonal fruits are an excellent starter for a brunch.

2	medium oranges, peeled and sectioned	2
1 cup	diced honeydew melon	250 mL
1 cup	fresh or frozen blueberries	250 mL
1 cup	sliced strawberries	250 mL
1	kiwifruit, peeled and chopped	1
2 tbsp	lime juice	25 mL
1 tsp	grated lime rind	5 mL
1 tsp	rum extract (optional)	5 mL
2 tbsp	unsweetened coconut	25 mL

• In bowl, combine oranges, melon, blueberries, strawberries and kiwifruit.
• Stir together lime juice, rind and rum extract, if using. Stir gently into fruit. Sprinkle with coconut and refrigerate for at least 30 minutes so flavours develop.

Makes 8 servings, 4 cups (1 L).
PREPARATION: 20 minutes
CHILL: 30 minutes or longer

Each serving: ½ cup (125 mL)

1 ◪ Fruits & Vegetables Choice

12 g carbohydrate, 1 g protein, 1 g fat, 2 g fibre, 54 kcal (230 kJ)

BROCCOLI AND HAM STRATA

Everyone enjoys this brunch recipe. Make the strata the night before, store in the refrigerator and bake in the morning.

6	slices multi-grain bread, cubed	6
1 cup	shredded light Cheddar cheese	250 mL
1 cup	shredded part-skim mozzarella cheese	250 mL
½ cup	diced ham	125 mL
1½ cups	broccoli or broccoflower florets	375 mL
¼ cup	chopped orange or red pepper	50 mL
4	eggs	4
2 cups	low-fat milk	500 mL
1 tbsp	Dijon mustard	15 mL
½ tsp	salt	2 mL
¼ tsp	pepper	1 mL

• Spray 13x9-inch (3.5 L) baking dish with non-stick coating. Place bread cubes in dish. Layer cheeses, ham, broccoli and orange pepper over bread.
• Beat eggs; combine with milk, mustard, salt and pepper. Pour over bread mixture. Cover and refrigerate for at least 3 hours or overnight.
• Bake in 350°F (180°C) oven for about 30 minutes or until set and top is golden brown. Cut into six squares.

Makes 6 servings.
PREPARATION: 25 minutes
CHILL: 3 hours or overnight
COOK: 30 minutes

Each serving: ⅙ of recipe

1½ ☐ Starchy Choices
1 ◆ 2% Milk Choice
2½ ◪ Protein Choices
1 ▲ Fats & Oils Choice

32 g carbohydrate, 26 g protein, 15 g fat, 4 g fibre, 354 kcal (1480 kJ)

CUCUMBER AND ORANGE SALAD

Serve this refreshing salad on Bibb or leaf lettuce.

6	leaves Bibb or leaf lettuce	6
½	medium English cucumber, thinly sliced	½
3	medium oranges, peeled and thinly sliced	3
¼ cup	chopped red onion	50 mL
¼ cup	chopped green pepper	50 mL

Dressing

½ cup	low-fat plain yogurt	125 mL
½ tsp	dried thyme leaves	2 mL
Pinch	freshly ground pepper	Pinch

• Arrange lettuce on large platter. Place cucumber and orange slices alternately in overlapping circles on lettuce. Sprinkle with onion and green pepper.
• Combine yogurt and seasonings. Spoon over salad. Cover and refrigerate for 1 hour before serving.

Makes 6 servings.
PREPARATION: 15 minutes
CHILL: 1 hour

Each serving: ⅙ of recipe

1 ◧ Fruits & Vegetables Choice

11 g carbohydrate, 2 g protein, 1 g fat, 2 g fibre, 54 kcal (230 kJ)

RHUBARB PUNCH

Tangy rhubarb makes a thirst-quenching beverage. Prepare this concentrate in large amounts when spring rhubarb is available, and freeze in small amounts for use throughout the year.

4	oranges	4
2	lemons	2
8 cups	sliced fresh or frozen rhubarb	2 L
4 cups	water	1 L
1 cup	granulated white low-calorie sweetener	250 mL

• Remove rind from oranges and lemons. Squeeze juice and reserve.
• In large saucepan, combine rhubarb, water, orange and lemon rind. Cover and cook over medium heat for 10 minutes or until rhubarb is tender.
• Remove from heat; stir in lemon juice and orange juice. Cool. Press through a sieve to remove rhubarb pulp; discard pulp.
• Add sweetener to strained juice. Pour into sterilized bottles and seal. Keep in refrigerator, or freeze for longer storage.
• To serve: Combine ⅓ cup (75 mL) punch concentrate with ¾ cup (175 mL) water, soda water or mineral water. Serve over ice cubes.

Makes 6 cups (1.5 L) punch concentrate.
PREPARATION: 20 minutes
COOK: about 10 minutes

Each serving: ⅓ cup (75 mL) concentrate

½ ◧ Fruits & Vegetables Choice

6 g carbohydrate, 1 g protein, 0 g fat, 1 g fibre, 23 kcal (100 kJ)

Poached chicken breasts become "gourmet" when served with Cranberry Coulis sauce. Keep the extra sauce for another occasion.

Cranberry Coulis Sauce

½ lb	fresh or frozen cranberries	250 g
1 cup	water	250 mL
4 tsp	lemon juice	20 mL
2 tsp	granulated sugar	10 mL
1	rind of 1 orange	1
1	juice of 1 orange	1
2 tbsp	granulated white low-calorie sweetener	25 mL

Chicken

2 cups	water	500 mL
1	bay leaf	1
2 tbsp	chopped onion	25 mL
2 tbsp	chopped celery leaves	25 mL
Pinch	salt and pepper	Pinch
4	boneless, skinless chicken breast halves (about 1 lb/500 g)	4

Cranberry Coulis Sauce

• In medium saucepan, cook cranberries, water, lemon juice, sugar, orange rind and juice over medium-low heat, for 8 to 10 minutes or until cranberries pop their skins. Press through a sieve or food mill. Stir in sweetener and refrigerate. Makes enough for 8 chicken breasts.

Makes 8 servings, 1½ cups (375 mL) sauce.
Each serving, 3 tbsp (45 mL) sauce.
PREPARATION: 10 minutes
COOK: 8 to 10 minutes

Chicken

• In skillet, bring water, bay leaf, onion, celery leaves, salt and pepper to boil. Add chicken; cover and simmer for about 15 minutes or until chicken is no longer pink inside. Remove from liquid; reserve liquid.*
• Serve each piece of chicken with 3 tbsp (45 mL) Cranberry Coulis.

Makes 4 servings and 1½ cups (375 mL) sauce.
PREPARATION: 5 minutes
COOK: 15 minutes

Each serving: one-half chicken breast and 3 tbsp (45 mL) sauce

½ ◪ Fruits & Vegetables Choice
3 ◪ Protein Choices

6 g carbohydrate, 27 g protein, 3 g fat, 1 g fibre, 164 kcal (690 kJ)

KITCHEN TIPS

• *Chicken broth: Pour liquid through a sieve; discard the cooked vegetables. Freeze to use when chicken broth is called for in a recipe.
• You can prepare the Cranberry Coulis ahead and freeze.

Ease the extra work special occasions often require. Make this dish ahead of time and reheat in the oven or microwave just before serving.

2 tsp	margarine or butter	10 mL
1½ cups	sliced mushrooms	375 mL
⅓ cup	chopped onion	75 mL
1 cup	pearl barley	250 mL
2½ cups	water	625 mL
2	chicken bouillon cubes **or** sachets chicken bouillon powder	2
¼ cup	chopped parsley	50 mL

• In saucepan, melt margarine over medium-high heat. Add mushrooms and onion; sauté for 3 to 4 minutes. Add barley, water and chicken bouillon. Cover and cook for about 30 minutes or until barley is tender. Stir in parsley and serve.

Makes 8 servings, 4 cups (1 L).
PREPARATION: 15 minutes
COOK: 30 minutes

Each serving: ½ cup (125 mL)

1 ▢ Starchy Choice
½ ▲ Fats & Oils Choice
1 ▰ Extra

*22 g carbohydrate, 2 g protein, 2 g fat,
4 g fibre, 106 kcal (440 kJ)*

BARLEY FACTS

• Barley is one of those whole grains rich in complex carbohydrate and soluble fibre

A mellow soup for fall and winter dinners. And yes, it can be frozen.

1 tbsp	margarine or butter	15 mL
1 cup	chopped onion (1 medium)	250 mL
2	leeks, chopped (white part only)	2
1½ cups	cubed potato (1 large)	375 mL
2 cups	cubed squash	500 mL
1 cup	thinly sliced carrot (2 medium)	250 mL
3 cups	chicken broth	750 mL
1½ cups	low-fat milk	375 mL
¼ cup	dry white wine **or** chicken broth	50 mL
	Salt and pepper	
	Chopped chives or green onions for garnish	

• In medium saucepan, melt margarine over low heat. Add onion and leeks and cook for 10 minutes; stir occasionally.
• Add potato, squash, carrots and chicken broth. Cover and cook on medium heat for about 20 minutes or until vegetables are tender. Cool slightly. Place in food processor or blender; purée until smooth.
• Return to saucepan; add milk and wine; season to taste. Cook on low heat until hot. Sprinkle with chives or green onions before serving.

Makes 8 servings, 8 cups (2 L).
PREPARATION: 20 minutes
COOK: about 30 minutes

Each serving: 1 cup (250 mL)

1 ▢ Starchy Choice
1 ▲ Fats & Oils Choice

*17 g carbohydrate, 5 g protein, 3 g fat,
2 g fibre, 113 kcal (470 kJ)*

This recipe makes more dressing than is needed to stuff two Cornish hens. However, it is so delicious you will be pleased to have extra to freeze for another occasion.

Dressing

3 tbsp	margarine or butter	45 mL
1 cup	chopped celery	250 mL
½ cup	chopped onion	125 mL
½ cup	chopped parsley	125 mL
2 cups	soft breadcrumbs	500 mL
1½ cups	cooked wild rice	375 mL
	(½ cup/125 mL uncooked)	
1	medium unpeeled tart apple,	1
	cored and chopped	
¼ cup	chopped pecans	50 mL
½ tsp	dried thyme	2 mL
½ tsp	salt	2 mL
¼ tsp	dried sage	1 mL
¼ tsp	pepper	1 mL
2	Cornish hens, thawed	2
	(each about 1¼ lb/625 g)	

KITCHEN TIPS

*• 4 cups (1 L) extra dressing sufficient for 4 hens.
• The dressing is also appropriate for a roast turkey.

Dressing
• In nonstick skillet, melt margarine. Add celery, onion and parsley and cook for 5 minutes.
• In medium bowl, combine celery mixture, breadcrumbs, wild rice, apple, pecans and seasonings.

• Rinse cavities of hens and pat dry with paper towelling.
• Stuff each hen with 1 cup (250 mL) dressing; close cavity with skewers or toothpicks. Place hens, breast side up, on rack in roasting pan.
• Roast hens in 350°F (180°C) oven for about 1 hour or until juices run clear and meat thermometer registers 170°F (80°C).
• To serve, place hens on cutting board and cut lengthwise through backbone. Serve one-half hen, stuffing side down, on each plate.

Makes 6 cups (1.5 L) dressing.*
Makes 4 servings, 4 Cornish hen halves with dressing.
PREPARATION: *20 minutes if wild rice is precooked*
COOK: *about 1 hour*

> **Each serving: ½ hen with ½ cup (125 mL) dressing.**
>
> ½ ☐ Starchy Choice
> 4 ☑ Protein Choices
> 1 ▦ Extra
>
> *12 g carbohydrate, 30 g protein, 12 g fat, 1 g fibre, 278 kcal (1160 kJ)*

SPICY PUMPKIN PIE

There are at least as many versions of pumpkin pie as there are provinces in Canada. We found this one to have a nice balance of spice to sweetness.

1	9-inch (23 cm) frozen pastry shell	1
1½ cups	canned pumpkin	375 mL
2	eggs, beaten	2
1 cup	low-fat milk	250 mL
3 tbsp	liquid calorie-free sweetener	45 mL
2 tbsp	packed brown sugar	25 mL
1 tsp	ground cinnamon	5 mL
½ tsp	ground nutmeg	2 mL
½ tsp	ground ginger	2 mL
¼ tsp	salt	1 mL
Pinch	ground cloves	Pinch
	Light vanilla ice cream (7% BF)	

• Prick pastry shell with a fork. Bake in 450°F (230°C) oven for 8 minutes.
• Stir together pumpkin, eggs, milk, sweetener, sugar and seasonings. Pour into partially baked pie shell.
• Bake in 350°F (180°C) oven for 50 minutes or until centre is almost set. Cool slightly and then refrigerate.
• Cut into 8 wedges and serve each wedge with 2 tbsp (25 mL) light vanilla ice cream.

Makes 8 servings.
PREPARATION: *15 minutes*
COOK: *50 minutes*

Each serving: ⅛ of pie with 2 tbsp (25 mL) light vanilla ice cream

½ ☐ Starchy Choice
½ ◪ Fruits & Vegetables Choice
1 ◧ 2% Milk Choice
1½ ◤ Fats & Oils Choices

20 g carbohydrate, 5 g protein, 9 g fat, 1 g fibre, 173 kcal (720 kJ)

BRAISED RED CABBAGE WITH CRANBERRIES

You'll be pleased with the ruby-red colour and the tart flavour of this unusual vegetable dish. Excellent served with turkey!

1 tsp	olive oil	5 mL
1 tbsp	brown sugar	15 mL
3 large	cloves garlic, crushed	3
1 cup	fresh or frozen cranberries, divided	250 mL
3 tbsp	red wine vinegar	45 mL
5 cups	shredded red cabbage (¾ lb/375 g)	1.25 L
⅓ cup	dry red wine	75 mL
Pinch	cayenne pepper	Pinch
	Salt and pepper to taste	

• In large saucepan, heat oil, brown sugar and garlic over medium heat for 2 minutes.
• Add ½ cup (125 mL) cranberries and vinegar. Cover and cook for about 5 minutes or until cranberries pop their skins.
• Add cabbage, wine and cayenne. Cover and cook on low heat for about 20 minutes or until cabbage is tender; stir occasionally.
• Stir in remaining ½ cup (125 mL) cranberries. Remove from heat; cover and let stand for 5 minutes or until cranberries are warm. Season to taste with salt and pepper. Serve hot or cold.

Makes 8 servings, 4 cups (1 L).
PREPARATION: *20 minutes*
COOK: *about 30 minutes*

Each serving: ½ cup (125 mL)

½ ◪ Fruits & Vegetables Choice

6 g carbohydrate, 1 g protein, 1 g fat, 1 g fibre, 32 kcal (130 kJ)

KITCHEN TIP

A food processor will make short work of shredding the cabbage.

CANADIAN DIABETES ASSOCIATION FOOD CHOICE SYSTEM

Knowing how to select the correct amount of food enables people with diabetes to plan meals that promote good diabetic control. The Food Choice System was created to make this easier.

Different foods contain different nutrients and affect blood glucose differently. For this reason, foods are grouped under six different headings: starchy foods, fruits and vegetables, milk, protein foods, fats and oils, and extras. Food Choice symbols are used to visually identify Food Groups.

To plan a meal, select one or more choices from each group according to a meal plan. This allows variety but also ensures that meals are balanced in carbohydrate (starch and sugar), protein and fat, as well as calories.

▢ STARCHY FOODS

Each Starchy Choice contains about 15 grams starch (carbohydrate) and 2 grams vegetable protein and supplies 68 calories of energy. Foods rich in complex carbohydrates, such as cereals, breads, pasta, rice, barley, dried peas and beans are all starchy foods. Each of the following is an example of 1 Starchy Choice: 1 slice bread, ½ medium potato, ½ cup (125 mL) cooked rice, corn, beans or pasta, 6 crackers.

◪ FRUITS & VEGETABLES

Each Choice from this group contains about 10 grams of sugar (carbohydrate) and 1 gram protein and supplies 44 calories of energy.

All fruits are high in natural sugar whether they are fresh, frozen, dried, canned or made into juice. Some vegetables such as peas, carrots, beets and squash also fit into this group. Examples of 1 Fruits & Vegetables Choice are: 1 small orange, ½ small banana, ½ medium apple, and ½ cup (125 mL) cooked peas or carrots.

◈ MILK

One Milk Choice is equal to ½ cup (125 mL) milk or yogurt.

Each serving contains about 6 grams milk sugar (carbohydrate), 4 grams protein and 0 to 4 grams fat, with anywhere from 40 to 80 calories, depending on butterfat (BF) content.

☑ PROTEIN FOODS

One Protein Choice contains about 7 grams protein and 3 grams of fat and provides about 55 calories. Lean meats, fish, and poultry fit into this group. So do eggs, peanut butter and most cheeses, but they contain more fat and calories. Examples: 1 egg or 25 grams of cheese is one Protein Choice; a chicken leg or pork chop may equal 3 or 4 Protein Choices depending on size and weight.

Dried peas and beans and soybean products are also high in protein (and low in fat) even though grouped with starchy foods.

▲ FATS & OILS

Each Choice in this group contains 5 grams of fat and provides 45 calories of energy. Examples are: 1 teaspoon (5 mL) margarine, butter or oil or 1 strip bacon.

▣ EXTRAS

Foods in this group contain little or no carbohydrate (starch or sugar) and have few calories (15 calories or less a serving).

Vegetables such as broccoli, salad greens, asparagus and cabbage fit this description. So do mustard and vinegar, lemon juice, herbs and spices. Extras add interest and flavour to meals.

The Canadian Diabetes Association (CDA) publishes the Food Choice System as the Good Health Eating Guide. It is available as a poster, pamphlet or book and may be obtained from a diabetes education centre or CDA office. It is most useful when used with a meal plan adapted to your eating pattern and energy needs.

INDEX

CHOICE MENUS QUESTIONNAIRE

In order to help serve you better, the Canadian Diabetes Association would like to hear from you. Please fill out this questionnaire and mail it to the address below.

1. Was this book purchased:

As a gift_____   For yourself_____

Other (please specify)_____

2. If the book was purchased by you, was your interest in reading about:

Heathy eating_____   Weight control_____

Diabetes_____   Meal planning_____

3. What did you like about the book?

Easy to use_____ Gives choices_____ Easier to manage a diet_____

4. What did you not like about this book?

Too difficult_____   Doesn't meet my needs_____

Other_____

5. What other information would be helpful to you?

Nutrition_____   Exercise_____

General Information on Diabetes_____

Information on the Canadian Diabetes Association_____

Other_____

6. If you would like more information, please fill out your name and address below:

Name:_____

Address:_____

City:_____   Province:_____

Postal Code:_____

Please detach questionnaire and mail to:
Canadian Diabetes Association, National Office, Attn: Coordinator of Special Projects
15 Toronto Street, Toronto, Ontario M5C 2R1